EAST OF SUPERIOR

John H. Gearey

EAST OF SUPERIOR

TRUE WILDERNESS STORIES

JOHN H. GEAREY

Belleville, Ontario, Canada

ISBN: 978-1-4600-0606-1
LSI Edition: 978-1-4600-0607-8
E-book ISBN: 978-1-4600-0608-5
(E-book available from the Kindle Store, KOBO and the iBooks Store)

Cataloguing data available from Library and Archives Canada

To order additional copies, visit:
www.essencebookstore.com

Guardian Books is an imprint of *Essence Publishing,* a Christian Book
Publisher dedicated to furthering the work of Christ through the written
word. For more information, contact:
20 Hanna Court, Belleville, Ontario, Canada K8P 5J2
Phone: 1-800-238-6376 • Fax: (613) 962-3055
Email: info@essence-publishing.com
Web site: www.essence-publishing.com

Printed in Canada
by
E**p**ic
P**ress**

DEDICATION

This book is dedicated to the memory of two good friends who loved nature and enjoyed the great outdoors.

To Ted Koski who enjoyed life as a trapper, hunter, log house builder, and gun collector. He was the all-around bushman who willingly helped so many others. He will be missed and fondly remembered.

To Derek Russell, a man who helped others in many different ways, from cooking meals on outdoor retreats to helping arrange and plan trips. His love of fishing and camping was contagious. He will be remembered as a man who loved nature and the thrill of catching a fish. We miss you.

TABLE OF CONTENTS

ACKNOWLEDGMENTS

To be very honest, many of these stories in this book could not have been written without the help of several people who were main participants in many of them. I wish to express my profound gratitude to Don Elliot (a wise 15 year old at the time who kept a journal and has a great memory), to Dean Love (a man also with a fabulous memory) and to Jean Koski, Jack McLeod, Roger White and Bill Autio for giving of their time to share their stories and digging out their journals and photos while challenging their memories of events from long ago.

I thank my son Robb so much for all his help in remembering his wild episodes in which he was fortunate enough to survive and my wife, Mary, who had to live through many of those experiences.

Finally, I thank Sherrill Brunton, Publishing Manager at Essence Publishing and Timothy Fransky, Project Editor, for all the good advice and time they have given with a deep appreciation to all the staff at Essence.

In all things I thank our Lord and Saviour Jesus Christ for His redeeming work at the cross.

THE AUTHOR

INTRODUCTION

Adventure in life can be both thrilling and terrifying. In the following pages I have written outdoor stories of people who endured hardship, trials and close encounters with death. Most of the stories are based on real life experiences intermixed with historical events with a smattering of humour. Throughout the book the outdoors is portrayed as what it is, beautiful and potentially deadly if precaution is not taken.

Although many of the stories involve possible disaster, the final story is from the mind of the author as he progresses into later life. As a disclaimer I have used literary license mostly in the area of dialogue to keep the stories interesting. Thus any words or thoughts used are fictional, and I apologize for any parts that some might remember differently.

Hopefully you will find the tales of these outdoor experiences as interesting and intriguing as I did when the people involved related them to me. From a fifteen year old teenager on a long canoe voyage to others who encountered desperate moments in nature, we can empathize and cheer them on through their wild experiences.

Happy reading,

THE AUTHOR

Dean, Ron, Ernie, and Andrew by the Wakami River

I. TERROR ON THE WAKAMI

Wilderness stories abound and some of those stories have moments of close encounters where life and limb hang in the balance. As you read this tale you may recall that moment of terror in your own life just before an impending car crash or a similar heart-pounding instance you will never forget. Such a moment came in the life of my friend Dean on the Wakami River.

The year was 1983, in mid May when Dean and three of his friends decided to run the Wakami River north of the town of Sultan in northern Ontario.

Our story begins as our four intrepid river runners have finished loading their two fifteen foot Oscar canoes with a week's supply of food and gear. They planned to paddle the river through Ridout Lake, Bayley Lake and down the Woman River to Horwood Lake, finishing the trip at the north end.

Two ladies stood on the shore and waved good-bye as the canoeists pushed off shore. Dean's wife, Linda, walked to her small car while Kathy, Ron's wife, headed for a large van parked a short distance away. They planned to drive to Chapleau and then east on Highway 101, hoping to find the dirt road to Horwood Lake and locate "Big Bear Camp." They would leave the van at the campground and the two women would drive the car back to their homes in Sault Ste. Marie.

Linda took the lead in her car and off they went down the road.

The time was early spring, before the pesky blackflies and mosquitoes made their appearance. The buds on the trees had formed but the foliage was more than a week away. In the northern bush, early in the springtime, moose come out to the roadside to drink the water and lick the surrounding vegetation that contains salt left from the winter salt trucks. Drivers must be careful as the big animals often stroll up onto the pavement where several are killed each year, usually during the night or the early light of the morning.

The two vehicles sped out to Highway 129 and then to Highway 101, which skirted the town of Chapleau. In a short time they had passed through the small community of Foleyet and began looking for a sign directing them to the "Big Bear Camp" on Horwood Lake.

Linda had her eyes peeled on the right side of the road when suddenly, a few yards in front of her a huge dark coloured animal climbed out of the ditch and up onto the main paved highway.

She was mesmerized for a moment as she watched the four legged beast saunter slowly in front of the car and come to stop as it watched them.

Coming to her senses, she slammed on the brakes and came to a screeching halt only a few feet from the biggest moose she had ever seen.

Truthfully she had not seen a great number of moose in her lifetime but she realized this bull moose was one big moose. The animal had stopped in the centre of the road blocking both lanes, his big head swaying back and forth as he eyeballed the vehicles. Kathy had stopped her van behind Linda's car and the ladies waited for the moose to move.

As Linda sat staring at the beast with her heart pounding, she began to have visions of the big bull charging the front of the car. She realized she had driven far too close for comfort and her car was far too small to withstand an attack from Mr. Moose. The huge beast could destroy the car and her too. All kinds of thoughts went through her mind. One thing had happened in the first few seconds after stopping. In her excitement she had pulled the lever for opening the hood mistakenly, instead of the emergency brake. Now she would have to get out and shut it before driving on.

Her eyes were glued on the stationary statue ahead of her when a knocking on the side window caused her to jump in her seat. Her friend was standing outside asking her to get out of the car. She rolled her window down with a questioning look.

"I think I'll stay inside, just in case I need to back up quick," Linda replied. She didn't trust the actions of the big bull as it kept a wild looking eye on them, lifting first one foot then the other. She couldn't believe it had not moved when Kathy had walked up from her van.

"Maybe that moose is sick and disoriented," remarked Linda, looking out the open side window.

"Come on and get out. That animal will move if we both jump around and yell. Usually they won't stand like that for very long with people nearby," Kathy replied.

"Ok. I'll get out but I'm leaving the door open just in case," she laughed nervously and climbed out of the car.

"Strange we haven't seen another vehicle since we stopped," Kathy said as she began to wave her arms. Linda soon followed suit adding a few short, high pitched yells.

At last the majestic animal casually moved off the paved surface of the road and headed down into the shallow ditch. The moose seemed to have no fear of cars or humans but somehow been able to survive and grow to an enormous size. Linda slammed the hood closed before getting back in the car.

She felt a little foolish for being uptight about this short encounter but felt relieved that all had turned out well. Thankfully she did not know what was transpiring at the same time on the river with her husband.

In the meantime the four canoeists had headed down the Wakami River with thoughts of the adventure that lay before them. The water level was very high so they were able to barrel through the shallow rocky rapids that later in the year would necessitate portaging. Flat rocks of all sizes lay below the surface with a few outcroppings, but the canoes skimmed swiftly over them. Several varieties of evergreens lined the shoreline. A few swampy areas had boulders barely under the surface which they managed to work their way through with care. The men stayed alert, watching for possible danger spots as they sped downriver.

Two hours went by. The day was warm but they knew the water would be ice cold as the lakes had only thawed a few days before. In wilderness trips they realized there was an element of good and bad attached to the planning. In their case the early spring brought colder days and nights, possibly snow storms and a short survival rate if someone fell out of a canoe.

On the other hand the water level is usually higher and swifter and consequently they would have far less portaging. The trip could often be completed much quicker and would give more time for fishing and shore time. However, the high water is often roily and the fish don't usually feed as well until the weather warms the water and the bugs start hatching.

The first two hours of the trip was a time of enjoying the beauty and tranquility of the remote area. A time to allow the serenity of the wilderness to envelop them and let the cares of everyday life slip into the far recesses of their minds. Each one in his own way had waited patiently for this special time away.

These four men still had vivid memories of two trips down another river in the past few years. They had challenged the famed Pukaskwa River that ran through the wilderness area known as Pukaskwa Park not far from the town of White River. The river had indeed been a challenge with dangerous rapids and some long, hard portages. Many tales from a few years past had persuaded the intrepid foursome to tackle the wild river. Always in search of the elusive speckled trout and some good adventure they had been able to successively navigate the river without mishap.

And now here they were on the Wakami River. This river should not hold the dangers the Pukaskwa River did, but well did they know how quickly mishaps can happen on a river in the north.

The father and son team of Ernie and Andrew were following Ron and Dean. They seldom spoke but stayed focused on their paddling and maneuvered around the many curves in the river.

Some fifty yards ahead, their friends were watching for underwater obstacles that could pose disaster, while discerning the current flow and best channels.

In a space of a few moments Ron and Dean came to a sharp bend of the river in the swift current. Ron tried to slow the canoe down as Dean peered ahead hoping to evaluate the rapids around the corner. Suddenly without notice an underwater rock stalled the canoe and spun them broadside to the upstream current. They had seen a number of flat rocks below the surface already but had till now avoided being hung up. The current was much stronger at this point and as they turned, a sweeper caught Dean in the chest and pulled him over and out of the canoe. Quick as a flash Ron and the canoe capsized and were swept down the river and into the bend.

A sweeper is a tree that has fallen into the river and has both limbs and branches in the water and above the water. Often a deciduous tree or an evergreen along the river bank will be ripped up by its roots and sent crashing into the water during a wind storm or flood. Other times the tree will simply splinter and the main trunk will fall into the river leaving some of the limbs and branches in the current with the remainder above the water. This presents a particularly dangerous situation in which several canoeists have lost their lives over the years when they were pulled into the tangled mass of limbs and swept off the canoe into the freezing cold water.

As Dean fell into the river he remained relatively calm and felt he would bob back up to the surface quickly as he wore an excellent life jacket. The shock of the frigid water was enough to stop the heart of a weaker man. The canoe had swung sideways after the spill and narrowly missed

Dean's head as Ron and the canoe careened downstream. Andrew and his dad were gripped by the strong current and were swept past their friends and into the bend before they could attempt a rescue.

Seconds went by as Dean attempted to resurface but for some reason he was unable to move and his head remained close to eighteen inches under water. He was not a man who panicked easily and had good lung power from playing squash on a regular basis and was in excellent physical condition. The spill had happened so quickly he had not been able to take in extra air and now his panic level began to rise as he attempted to pull himself free from the unseen trap below.

He knew he only had a few precious seconds before his strength gave out from the lack of oxygen and he would pass out.

Through the years a few people who have survived have talked about their close encounter with death when they had but seconds left to save themselves. Drowning has taken many lives over the years and Dean knew this could be his time.

With his mind racing, two thoughts came clear as he tugged and pulled at whatever had grasped his life jacket and was holding him down. He knew his wife Linda would be really upset and even angry at him if he perished, as it would leave the raising of the kids to her alone. He still remembers what he said to himself in those first few seconds. "I'm dead and Linda's going to kill me."

The other thought was a silent cry for help from God.

His lungs felt like bursting as he reefed and tore at the jacket to get it off. Dean reached up and grasped a small limb and tried to pull himself up to the surface by one arm

19

while looping a leg over the extended branch. With his last remaining strength he was able to get his nose and mouth just above the water level while laying horizontal, which allowed him to breathe again. He knew he did not have long to disengage himself from whatever was holding the life jacket in a solid grip. His energy would fade quickly in the icy water as he kept pulling himself upwards in order to get more air into his lungs.

Dean was frantic and now he became further frustrated because he couldn't find the plastic snaps to his life jacket. With his one free arm he kept fumbling with his numb fingers. He tried over and over again to locate the snaps but to no avail.

Once more he prayed as hope was fading fast. "Lord, if I am to get out of this I need your help right now." Almost instantaneously a picture came to his mind with the thought, "The snaps are up around my throat." Quickly he reached up and unsnapped them and then tried pulling out his one free arm. He couldn't get the jacket off his shoulder; it was too tight and the force of the current kept it pinned to him.

At this point there might be some who simply would give up and let nature take its course. Not Dean. His mind did not allow him to succumb to the cold and his weakening condition. With a huge degree of willpower he did a bodybuilder type of chest flex and swelled up with what strength he had left and then with a mighty effort he pulled forward in the hope the life jacket would give way.

Not being a man of great size or massive strength some might say what he attempted was only an act of sheer desperation, that had little hope of succeeding. And maybe that is true. However Dean knew that all is possible to those who put their trust in God.

How many would think they could burst the seams of a life jacket under any circumstances. However God was not ready to let this young man die so early in life.

Riiipp! The life jacket suddenly gave way and split down the back. This loosened the jacket a little and allowed Dean to pull one arm free and then grasping the branch with the other hand he was able to get his other arm out.

Finally, he managed to get his upper body above water and breathe properly but realized he was still some twenty yards from shore and feeling exhausted.

At the very moment he was able to extricate himself from the clutches of the fallen tree he heard a voice. By this time Ron had managed to swim to shore with the canoe and was yelling at him. "Are you ok? What can I do?"

"Throw me a rope and I'll grab it," Dean shouted.

Ron made a good throw and the rope landed close to his chum who was hanging on to a limb of the tree. Dean's adrenalin had dropped and his stamina was decreasing rapidly but he reached out and grabbed the rope and with one hand wrapped it around his waist and tied a knot in it.

At this point he released his grip on the tree branch and swung out into the current. All the years of playing water polo and training as a life guard came into play as the swift water pulled him downstream. He had planned to head for shore in a small bay and change his clothes but soon realized within a few strokes he no longer had the strength he usually had. His whole body was sluggish. He also knew that most experts in water survival claim a human has only about fifteen minutes of normal functioning when immersed in water that is close to the freezing mark. Time was passing quickly.

Ron had held onto the end of the rope that Dean was attached to but let go believing his chum had made it to shallow enough water that he could stand up and make it to shore on his own. Unfortunately the water was still over Dean's head and he was forced to keep swimming. Without a life jacket he could move far easier but his clothes were water laden and heavy. He felt his strength ebbing away and realized he had some distance left to swim. Hypothermia had set in from being in the frigid water for so long and that brought a feeling he had never felt before. He began to feel lethargic and didn't seem to care what happened to him.

He quit swimming and let his feet down hoping the water was shallow enough for him to touch bottom. Nothing. No bottom. Dean sank below the surface. His head went out of sight.

His weakened state screamed within him. "Don't give up, start swimming or you're going to die." With the last bit of willpower he began to swim once more. He had to make it all the way to shore this time or he would definitely drown.

The will to live enabled Dean to finally come to within a few feet of dry land. His feet scraped the bottom but he was too weak to stand so he crawled through the last remaining water and fell on the shoreline.

Although his brain no longer functioned properly something told him to get his wet clothes off. He struggled to rise from the ground but was totally exhausted and weak. He hoped he had the energy to start a fire but soon realized the sun had come out and the rays felt good on his face. He was surprised at how warm the air temperature was, and thought maybe he would warm up once he had on dry clothes.

A voice from a distance away came to him. "Dean, thank God you made it."

Twisting a little he looked down the shoreline. His friend walked over to him. As Ron approached he could tell Dean was in a weakened state and needed help. "You get out of those wet clothes and rub yourself down with my old shirt here." Ron handed over a heavy shirt he had managed to dig out of a waterproof bag that had been secured in the front of the canoe. Thankfully the sun had warmed the morning air and he knew how much different they would feel if it had been raining and cold.

"Hey guys, are you ok?" Someone was yelling at them. A few minutes later Ernie and Andrew arrived carrying some extra supplies.

"I'll get some dry clothes out of your duffle bag, Dean." Ernie began untying a big bag from the canoe Ron had brought to shore. "It looks like your waterproof bag is not as good as it should be. Some of your clothes are damp."

"I'll put them on anyway," Dean replied. With the numbness in his body he could barely move. He needed to raise his body temperature and soon.

"You lost some of your equipment, guys, and all of your fishing gear. Rods, reels and tackle are all gone," Andrew said, looking into the bottom of the canoe.

"Well, I give thanks to the Lord I'm not gone," Dean replied.

"Yeah, you don't need a fishing rod anyway. You never catch any fish, ha ha ha," Ernie giggled. Someone had dug out some granola bars for Dean to chew on while he tried to warm himself after removing his wet clothes and putting on the dry ones.

Ernie watched his friend for any sign of weakness, wondering how much effect the time spent in the freezing river would have on him. As far as he could tell the man was recovering quickly, probably due to the good physical condition he was in.

"How do you feel, Dean? Are you warming up?" Andrew asked.

"I sure am feeling better than I was ten minutes ago," came the reply. "That sun has really warmed me up and I am ready to have another go at it."

After some discussion it was agreed they would head down the river for a few more miles before stopping for the night.

The miles slipped by as the group paddled effortlessly through some marshy areas and around more bends in the river. Due to the high water in the river they were able to speed through some challenging rapids that later in the summer would not be navigable. Even with the water as high as it was they barely skimmed over some of the flat rocks below the surface. Dean wondered if he could sustain another dunking like the last one. A couple of the rapids were dangerous enough that portaging would have been a far safer option. However they only pulled off the river twice to walk around two sets of rapids that had boulders showing above water.

Fortunately there were no more life threatening mishaps as the day wore on, but the map had shown rapids and a four hundred yard portage coming up just before Little Ridout Lake, where they planned to stop for the night. They continued past rocky granite ledges and in one section of the river a number of cedars hung over the water, making for dynamic scenery. To their disappointment they saw no moose or bear. Perhaps the animals were waiting for warmer weather to come down to the water for a drink or swim. They decided to take a midday break and while Ron and Dean went ashore for lunch, Ernie and Andrew headed out for some fishing on the river. A half hour later they came back from their quest with no fruit from their endeavours. The pair guided the canoe into shore. As the craft ground into the soft gravel, Andrew stepped from the bow and gave the canoe a reef to bring it further up on land.

Sadly he failed to look back at his dad, who had begun to rise from his seat in the stern. The immediate result of his action was to send Ernie flying in the air in a majestic back flip directly into the cold water. As he headed downstream splashing and kicking he could be heard yelling. "I'm going to kill him! I'm going to kill him!" At 5'2" and with his short stubby legs thrashing in the water the scene was too much for the other three, and they all began to roar with laughter.

Dean was feeling exhausted and knew he would enjoy a solid supper and a good nights rest but the group decided to keep canoeing to make up for lost time. A short while later they heard rapids and after stopping for a look decided to run them, which would move them into Little Ridout Lake. Little Ridout and Ridout Lake are expansions of the Wakami River, both having shallow water and marshy areas. They paddled slowly forward on the lake in the waning moments of the day and finally saw a campsite on the north side on top of a high rock. Here they would camp for the night.

The night passed uneventfully and the next day found the four canoeists paddling through Little Ridout and running a short rapids that brought them to Ridout Lake, which was a larger version of the previous one. Once through they were back into swifter water with sections of river that meandered under more overhanging trees. Some time later they heard the rumble of what they assumed was a large waterfall not far down the river. As they drew closer the sound intensified and they looked for a spot to disembark but they were unable to locate a portage sign or a place to pull into. Within minutes they had come precariously close to the edge. Quickly the canoes were steered towards shore and at the last moment the men saw an opening and with several strong strokes brought the canoes to land.

Much relieved the foursome exited their canoes and clambered down the rocky slope of the portage in order to view the frothing mass of white water that fell some fifty feet into a large pool below. The double lip waterfall was spectacular and would have proven to be disastrous if they had not found the opening to the portage. The trail was steep and slippery and the trip down with the canoes and packs was extremely treacherous.

Although Andrew had tried out his trusty fishing pole and his favourite pickerel lure earlier to no avail, he was determined to catch supper from below the falls. However, as when he trolled in the lake he was unable to entice a fish of any kind. Sadly he put away his equipment and they headed back on the river.

The day wore on as they canoed through Ransom Lake, another expansion of the river, and on down the Wakami River through two more sets of rapids to Bayley Lake.

Once on Bayley Lake they could see stands of birch and spruce interspersed with outcrops of rock. The men were tiring and hoped to find a campsite but paddled the length of the lake and soon were back on the river. Some ten minutes later they found a good spot and pulled in for the night.

The weather had turned from sun to cloud with a light drizzle. The temperature was dropping and they knew from past experience they must prepare for a cold night. They would build a large fire and eat a good supper to give them energy for the next day. Like many outdoorsmen they carried "Magic Pantry," which came in a foil pouch and had a variety of meals that tasted good. The men put the pouches in water and boiled them for five minutes in a metal container and then put the meals ready to eat on their plates. Afterwards they ate fruit from a can and washed it all down with Lipton black tea. All good, but the friends knew tomorrow would be a challenge by the feel of the low front that was moving in.

Morning arrived. Dean peered out the door and then looked back at Ron, his partner, who had just opened his eyes.

"Feels cold out there," Ron said, looking to see if Dean was getting out of the tent.

"You have that right, and wait till you see what else."

"What do you see?" Ron asked.

"Dress warm and be ready for a cold day on the water. Snow has covered everything," Dean replied as he exited the tent.

The group dusted the snow from their equipment and started a fire. In a short time the water was boiling while the men chewed on granola bars. They had donned rain jackets to keep from getting wet from the snow. By now a bitter wind had come up and ice pellets stung their faces. Gone was the sunshine and warm weather they had enjoyed the first two days.

The men were not long in loading the canoes and pushing off shore. No thoughts of fishing on this day, only getting down the river.

As the day progressed the team ran five more rapids and after a sharp corner in the river they entered the Woman River and headed north. They sped quickly along and passed the merging Opeepeesway River. The snow had gradually turned into a light rain, making the going tough. Two portages brought them to a smaller falls they needed to portage around. The trails were wet and slippery underfoot and exceedingly dangerous.

Once again on the water they swept past the entrance to the Rush River and shortly found themselves portaging around another small falls.

Miserable and cold, the group of four looked forward to finding a campsite. They had paddled a long way and were wearing down. However, two more portages, each one over six hundred yards awaited them.

As they finished the last portage around Horwood Falls they came to a campsite where they would stay the night.

Exhausted, the men pulled out their camping gear and set up. After supper was finished the men gladly turned in after the long day on the river. Each one gave thanks to God for the safety through the day as the portages were wet and slippery where anyone could have slipped and broken bones. One more day awaited them, paddling the length of Horwood Lake, which could easily turn out to be a tough haul depending on the wind direction.

Four days had passed since they began their trip. With sunshine the first day and cloud the next, the trip had begun well. Then came the rain, cold and snow and they now wondered what awaited them on the remaining day.

The morning arrived, bleak and cold with a wind out of the north. As the four friends scurried around, eating breakfast and packing up the tents and equipment, each one secretly felt glad they were heading home.

Once the men had loaded the canoes they headed north out on the lake and down a long arm around 9 a.m. At first all seemed good with only a slight breeze and a light ripple on the water but within a short time the wind increased and the waves grew larger. Now they had to constantly angle the canoes to keep from going broadside. At times they felt they were hardly making any progress against the wind and waves. The waves created great swells and once as Dean looked sideways he felt a moment of panic. His friends in the other canoe were nowhere to be seen. At the top of the next crest he caught sight of them just as they plunged into a deep trough. As the hours went by, their arms and backs screamed for rest but they had no choice but to keep going.

The lake grew rougher and the men worked throughout the day, using as much strength as they could muster to make headway. As one man put it later, "It was a horrendous trip." At any time and with one slight mistake a canoe could have swamped or tipped over. Disaster would have resulted with the great possibility of tragedy. The trip had begun with a time of terror for Dean and ended with a ten hour day of desperate paddling on Horwood Lake for all four canoeists.

The group closed the distance rapidly once the lodge came into view, and with the end in sight they made one final push.

Relief mixed with fatigue was evident on each man's face as the canoes landed safely on the beach.

The exhausted men expressed their thankfulness to the Lord for arriving safely on the shores of Big Bear Camp. During that day each man, a faithful believer, had prayed they would make it across the wide expanse of the lake safely. In closing, the men's strong faith in God gave them the strength they needed to make it through their harrowing experience.

2. MIRACLE ON MASH LAKE ROAD

A long time has passed since this remarkable tale happened. In years long past, the Mash Lake Road was used for hauling out logs from the interior of Lake Superior Park. At the time of this story, logging trucks were allowed to use the road as well as a few cars travelling to cabins on Sand Lake. However all other motorized vehicles were not allowed and hiking down the dusty roads was the usual method for accessing the lakes.

It was during one of my earliest trips with my chums in which we had carted in a canoe and a rubber raft, that we happened to come upon two well hidden canoes near one of the lakes. We had only recently read the posted rules that outlawed leaving canoes in the park. Did that mean we could use them if we happened to be on the lake? My friends didn't see a problem with that along with many others.

In the wisdom of youth neither did I, and looking back now, using those canoes was only one of many questionable decisions that led to my young son being put in harm's way.

The day began early one bright morning, on the first day of a long weekend in August for my wife and I and our twelve year old son. We entered the Mash Lake Road accompanied by Chico, a close friend with whom I had fished and canoed for some time. We parked across the highway that led to Wawa, the nearest town, and prepared to roll down the well graded dirt road on our bicycles. In the early years of the park there were no signs that disallowed bikes, at least none we could see. We knew as well, the loggers didn't work on the weekends, so we felt reasonably safe on the road. That was a miscalculation. Danger lurks around every corner in many different guises.

With our packs securely strapped on our backs we sped away heading for our dream lake. We soon found that using bikes did not make the trip a whole lot easier, at least on the way in.

"Whew! That was a steep one," exclaimed Chico after pushing his bike to the top of the first hill he encountered. The rest of us were sucking air trying to replace the oxygen we had used climbing the hill.

"How far did you say it was to where you saw those canoes stashed?" my wife asked. She was beginning to wonder if this trip was such a great idea after all.

"From my calculations we should have between five to six miles on this road and then we will bushwhack for a half a mile through the woods to the canoes," I responded, carefully avoiding looking into my wife's eyes.

"That doesn't sound too far, does it?" her voice dripped with sarcasm as she sat down on the bicycle seat and began to pedal away.

Chico was looking at me with a grin on his face. "You didn't tell her there are four more hills to go and this was the shortest one."

"No, but she'll find out in time," I replied, as I mounted my 12-speed bike with its narrow tires.

My son Robb was pedalling a 20" bike with fat tires, which I hoped would give him better stability. The road was mostly packed hard but some spots had loose gravel that could easily send a bike sliding out of control.

Safety concerns were never a real concern for any of us thirty or forty years ago. Thinking back on those days, no one took safety seriously, regardless what sport or activity you were involved in.

Why not, you may ask? I will digress for a moment in the story to say that the culture was different. "Real men" did not wear helmets for safety in those days. Gordie Howe was one of my heroes and he and other hockey players never wore helmets. Seldom if ever anyone wore a helmet when cycling, regardless of age. In the north those of us and our predecessors who ran rapids never wore helmets for safety. As the first snowmobiles came out, it took years before real "bushmen" would wear anything but a toque. The answer of course to the question why is found in the pride of man. No man wanted to look like a sissy so we would never don anything that made us look weaker in the eyes of other men. Time has changed and even the rough and tumble men of today have changed.

We continued pedalling down the road and soon came to hill number two; this hill was much longer and steeper than the first one. The sun had risen above the trees and the summer heat was already affecting us as we trudged up the grade, pushing the bikes before us.

I wished we had come earlier but here we were, already breathing hard and sweating heavily.

Another half hour found us at the top of the hill and pedalling on a long flat stretch with a renewed energy. Unfortunately the great feeling did not last long as we soon were moving up another hill, huffing and puffing up what appeared to be a never ending rise in the road.

"This is the longest climb, isn't it, John?" Chico asked as he slowed and dismounted.

"Yes, this hill is a slow and steady climb for nearly half a mile with two steep sections, which will be fast to come down."

Our son Robb was already labouring and breathing hard and was quietly muttering to himself. His mother was doing a little better but we had a long way to go.

"Keep thinking how great coming back will be, going like crazy down these grades. We won't have to pedal at all, just hang on for dear life," I said, hoping to keep everyone moving forward.

After the long slow haul up the hill we took a well deserved rest and then pedalled for a short distance before climbing the last major grade. By now the day was very warm and we were drinking a lot of water. Chico and I had the heavy sacks and were beginning to sag from the weight. Yes, the trip out would be so much easier, going down these wild hills.

Our ride and walk into the far away lake took over three hours but we finally arrived, hot, sticky and tired at the spot we would hide the bikes. We then began our walk through the bush in search of the hidden canoes. In a short time we were able to find them in the same place we had last seen them, along with the paddles. After loading the canoes we soon were heading down the lake with the breeze blowing through our clothes.

On this trip the fishing was spectacular and we caught some beautiful speckled trout and had some great camp-fires. Two days later after a restful weekend away from work, we were back on the main road, heading home.

"I'm sure looking forward to going down those hills," Chico said as he straddled his bike. "Just be careful and keep your speed down or you could lose control."

"Yes, that's for sure," Mary replied, "Some of those hills are long and have lots of gravel on them. It would be easy to skid out and go for a tumble."

The four of us began our trip back, feeling good and without a worry. Hopefully we would be back to the truck in half the time it took us to come in.

Our son was a little daredevil and now was his turn to really cruise. He had in the last few years developed a disregard for his own safety. We all knew that the speed we could attain going down this road could spell disaster. I was definitely worried as he charged ahead.

During the first mile or so he would slow down enough for us to get closer and then away he would go. I as a parent was definitely concerned of his seemingly reckless abandonment of safety as he whirled ahead at rocket speed.

At the top of the longest and steepest hill, I paused and looked down the section of road where he could hit speeds that would put fear in the heart of most adults. Sadly I knew from past experience, whether biking or skiing, Robb loved to show his dad how fearless he was.

We could hear nothing with the wind whistling past our ears, as we vainly tried to stay close to the young man. Down the longest hill, Chico and I cruised at high speed, with Mary not far behind. We tried to stay in control but often simply hung on for dear life. Twice I hit gravel that nearly sent me over the handlebars and was saved by the closest of margins.

As I came down the middle grade I could see my son disappearing over the lip of the steepest part of the road. I braked carefully during the descent as my confidence was already shaky from the two close calls I'd had already. Coming to the spot where I had last seen Robb, I had a good view from the top of the rise for at least four hundred yards and there was no sign of him. I came to a full stop and began to have a queer sensation in the pit of my stomach. Where was the young fellow? There was no way he could go fast enough to make it around the far corner in the road so quickly.

Mary and Chico had come alongside and were wondering what had happened. Worry and fear grew rapidly in our minds as we stared ahead down the road.

"Where is he?" Chico asked as he began looking down at the ground trying to find Robb's tire marks.

I dismounted and began walking about on the road. The section was partially sandy with loose gravel and then I saw tire marks made by a bike going down the hill. Chico was already following the marks to where he could see skid marks in the sand heading for the side of the road.

"Come here John and look at this." Chico motioned for me to come to closer. He was standing on the side of the road looking down.

As I walked over my chest began to restrict as I was fearful of what he was going to show me. This did not look good.

I will never forget the feeling that rushed through me as I came alongside of my friend and looked down to where he was gazing. At the side of the road was a steep hundred foot drop with lots of boulders that were close together and some were very sharp and dangerous looking. Threaded among the mess of rocks were a number of good sized trees.

However the strangest thing was what we didn't see. We could see no sign of Robb. Where was he? Why was he not in sight?

Chico and I looked at each other in bewilderment as we stared down through the rocks and trees. We definitely could see where the bike marks had headed over the cliff and then nothing. No bike and no Robb.

I yelled down hoping our son had survived the steep drop, remembering stories of youngsters dying or being crippled from bad bicycle accidents. I slowly began my descent down the steep grade looking for some sign of him. Suddenly, a short distance down I saw his bike laying beside a big boulder. He must have somehow stayed seated till he hit the rock and then was propelled down the rest of the hill.

Raising my voice once more I was almost in panic mode. Thoughts of him laying at the bottom of the hill either dead or his body smashed up, were almost paralyzing me. He was not responding to my calling as I moved further down, casting about, hoping to see him. All I could see were rocks and trees. I knew it was impossible for him not to be hurt with so many obstacles blocking his down hill fall.

At last I reached the bottom of the grade and sure enough, there lay my son in a fetal position. He did not move or respond when I kneeled beside him and began speaking to him. As I rubbed his face he began to revive a little and stared listlessly at me.

"Robb, did you hit your head on the way down? Where does your body hurt?" I asked with trepidation. "Don't try to move yet."

I began to feel over his body for broken bones. In the meantime he had sat upright and had become fully conscious. Fear was beginning to turn to hope, the hope that beyond any reasonable expectation he had somehow survived the steep fall through the tangle of birches, poplars and sharp rocks.

"I think I'm ok, Dad. My head hurts a little and my one arm is sore but I'll be alright."

"Let's try to stand, my boy," I said and helped him to his feet.

His legs seemed to be undamaged, though he moved a lot slower than usual. I yelled up to his mother and Chico to let them know I had found him and that he appeared to be in reasonably good shape.

"We're coming up," I shouted with a choking feeling in my throat knowing somehow, miraculously, the young man had survived what looked like certain disaster. To this day we are convinced God kept him safe as he plunged down the steep incline through the boulders and trees. Not only did he survive but he was able to make it on his own back to the truck.

Although he was sore for some time, it was not long before he was flying again on his trusty bike.

Lessons learned. While we can't always control the things that impact the decisions we make, we can move ahead and use those lessons to grow in wisdom as we put our trust in the Lord. Although Mary and I took our two children into that remote lake a year later, we never rode the bikes in again. We hiked in to what we now call "Golden Pond" and had no mishaps.

We will always give thanks to God for the miracle that happened that day.

Don and Dave paddling the Albany River

3. A YOUNG MAN'S JOURNEY ON THE ALBANY

INTRODUCTION:

The Albany River is situated in northwestern Ontario, 320 km north of Thunder Bay. The river is 982 km long and is the second longest and largest river in the province of Ontario. Originally called the "Chichewan," the Cree word meaning "many rivers in one going to ocean," it was used as a fur trader route beginning in 1675.

The Hudson's Bay Co. (HBC) built the first outpost between 1675-79 on the mouth of the Albany River as it flows into James Bay and in 1683 named the fort and river after the Duke of Albany, who later became King James II. The first inland post was built in 1743 at the converging of the Albany and the Kenogami rivers but later the Osnaburgh House on Osnaburgh Lake was more successful.

Along the shores of the Albany River several Cree and Ojibway villages have dwelled for centuries, existing on hunting, fishing and trapping. Tourism and guiding have also begun to spring up in the latter years. The Cambrian Shield falls away at the Ogoki River and the distance from there to James Bay is 400 km.

Over the past 300 years a range of watercraft have travelled the famous Albany River, from York boats to kayaks. Many are the wild stories, from a one man survival story to large groups of canoeists who have paddled, rowed, motored and even sailed parts of the river. The story following is of a group of ten teenagers and two adult leaders as they challenged one of the most isolated rivers in Canada.

IN THE BEGINNING:

Fifteen year old Don had a rough time in the van during the night managing only two hours sleep. He was not a happy camper and noticed several of the other youth were edgy and somewhat irritable as well. Two vans full of teenagers and camping gear had travelled from the city of Sault Ste. Marie and were finally pulling into the camping area on Lake Osnaburgh. The long drive had been tiring but they had finally arrived at the starting point of their planned 500 mile canoe trip down the mighty Albany River.

Don's dad was Bob Elliott, who had graciously driven the van and would travel back home alone after supper. Don was very proud of his father, who was a renowned carver and craftsman who had won many awards in North America. He had a number of his carvings distributed throughout the world to well known individuals including state and world leaders.

As the group spilled out of the extended van, Bob agreed to cook a meal before he headed back home. Everyone was tired and sluggish but once the tents were erected they sat around devouring the tasty Alaskan spaghetti meal set before them. When supper was over,

Bob climbed into his van and headed back down the road while many of the exhausted youth went into their tents.

The following morning found the group eager to be on the river and ready for some excitement after their dragged out trip in the van. Don was matched with Dave Collins in a sixteen foot Peterborough Algonquin Cruiser built in 1932. The canvas-covered heritage canoe was in pristine condition and Don and his dad both hoped it would survive the long trip through the boulder strewn rapids they were sure they would encounter.

"Good morning, Arnold. Looks like a great day," said Abe Janzen, the group leader and planner. Abe was actively involved as a missionary in the north with an organization called the Shantymen. Abe was a sturdy, strong individual who thoroughly loved the outdoors and had spent many hours in lumber camps and native settlements preaching and sharing his love for Christ. Although involved in pastoral duties, he seemed to find time to lead groups of teenagers on river runs almost every year. Only three years before he had led another large group down the Albany when the river was very high.

"Well, everyone seems to be in better spirits this morning," Arnold Collins, the other adult leader, replied. He enjoyed spending time in the outdoors and on this trip he had brought his two teenage sons along. Arnold, a tall man with a wiry strength, was efficient in repairing and mending and making useful articles that would be handy to have on these trips. Gord, one of his sons, would be in the same tent as Don. He looked for David, his other son, and realized he and Don were already in their canoe, patiently waiting for the rest. " Those two are always anxious to go," he thought to himself.

"Let's get everything loaded," Abe sang out. He noticed his two sons, Tom and Tim, had already loaded their canoe and had drifted off shore.

The canoes finally were on the water, and the excitement built as the sun's rays reflected off the surface of the lake into their eyes.

Noon hour brought rain and a beautiful rainbow that encompassed the sun—a sight many had never seen before. Quickly each canoe covered their supplies with clear plastic tarps as the rain pelted down. The date was July 22, 1976 and this type of weather was not unusual with warm summer showers mixed with sunshine through the day.

The changing weather patterns had little affect on the paddlers as they flew down the lake with the wind to their backs. Don and David surged ahead in the old Peterborough canoe. The narrow beam and sleek design facilitated the young men's paddling and they were soon far ahead of the rest; however Don, even in his youth, was safety conscious and often held back for the others to run the rapids before he did. He reasoned that by watching the others he could tell which channels in the river were safer and thus make a wiser decision.

Suddenly the pair could see the beginning of shallow rapids with a number of dangerous looking rocks rising out of the water.

"Let's get to shore as fast as we can," sang out Don in the stern of the canoe. "Look out," he yelled as they scraped a rough looking boulder.

"That was a bad one, Dave. We'd better get out and line the canoe through this. I'll look to see if we tore the canvas on Dad's canoe."

The two young men climbed out and began to line the canoe close to shore in the swift moving water. The others moved towards them and began making their way through the shallow, rock strewn water. Suddenly Dave lost his grip on the gunwale and the bow broke loose with Don hanging on, his legs bouncing off the rocks. His heart sank as the canoe swamped and filled with water.

"All our gear is going to be soaked," moaned Dave as he pulled the front end of the canoe up on shore at the tail end of the rapids so they could examine the old Peterborough for damage.

"I see a long deep scratch on the bottom but it didn't go through. My dad will understand but won't be happy," Don mumbled after looking the canoe over. "The good news is that our stuff hardly got wet. Good thing we packed everything in plastic."

The others had finally made it through and were taking their time landing on the shoreline. Phil and Tom already on shore were describing in detail how they had swamped coming through the wavy rapids. It had been a long difficult half mile of lining through the rough water.

"Wait a minute!" cried Don looking around with an anguished look on his face. "I lost my dad's favourite knife. It must have fallen out of the sheath." In deep frustration he began to walk in the water back upstream.

"How could I lose Dad's favourite knife that he let me use?" he muttered under his breath as he moved upstream against the current. He carefully looked down in the water hoping against hope that he would see the missing knife.

His heart was broken as he recalled the deep scratch on the side of the canoe and now his failure to secure an item like the knife that was so useful on a camping trip.

Young Don had already begun to acquire the traits of a thoughtful, keenly intelligent individual who would one day be an accomplished city engineer.

However, for the moment his only thought and prayer was to find the missing knife. Then as if a hand from above had directed him he saw a flash in the water.

"I see it, I see it!" he yelled to his friend. Sure enough he could see a shiny blade sticking straight up with the handle jammed between two rocks.

"Wow! How dangerous is that, Don?" Dave responded when he saw the knife only a foot or so under the water. "Everyone came through this way and somehow missed seeing it."

"I can only imagine what kind of damage that would have done to someone's foot if they had stepped on it. An injury like that would necessitate turning back and taking them out for proper medical treatment."

With a sigh of relief Don lashed the knife to the sheath and thanked God for keeping everyone safe from what could have been a grievous accident. This trip was not beginning as well as he hoped. Deep inside he wished he could be with his family enjoying the yearly vacation at Skookum Lake. He always had such great fun there each summer, but here he was instead starting out on a long canoe trip that already had caused him grief.

The rain finally stopped as they continued on and a few hours later they located a rocky beach and decided to camp for the night. Darkness was encroaching but Gary, the youngest crew member, who loved to fish at any time went for a short paddle and caught two pike and three pickerel and shared them at supper time with the others.

The following day began with sunshine and a few clouds as the group headed down river. Don knew they were far too late leaving the campsite at 11:30 a.m. Already the day was difficult for him as he had developed blisters on his legs from sunburn that had become quite painful.

After a few hours of intense paddling, Abe called for a stop at a narrow strip of beach on their left. "Everyone land and we'll have lunch and take a bath."

Don and his partner pulled into the sandy area ahead of the others. "I'm going for a swim and take a bath before we eat," said Don.

The two young men soon found their swim trunks and were already in the water as the other canoes pulled ashore.

"Does that ever feel good, Dave. I feel like living again," gurgled Don as he came out of the water. "Let's eat some of our Kraft dinner with salmon and peas. I'm famished."

After a short respite they were off down the river paddling with renewed vigour. Abe had warned them to watch for rough waters ahead and within a half hour they came up to them.

"Let's run this set of rapids," Dave suggested as they entered what appeared to be a shallow but swift part of the river.

The canoe skimmed over two large flat rocks just under the surface and then bounced off a large boulder and slid into another rock. They heard a loud noise. "Crack, craaack!!"

"That does not sound good." Don was looking along the inside of the canoe at the cedar planking. "We've cracked the wood in two places but we're not taking on water yet."

Once again young Don felt bad and continued to think of Skookum Lake and all the fun he was missing.

In a few minutes the others came through the rapids safely with only one accident. Abe's son, Tim, had rammed his father's canoe and snapped a rib high in the bow. A close call, and everyone was happy to come through without any other serious mishap.

The maps showed Kagami Falls around the next bend. Some of the others were convinced it was at least two bends away. Making the correct decision where the portage was located would be critical.

Don pointed to the map Arnold was holding. "I am sure the portage is right around the next bend on the left side," Arnold concurred.

A long discussion erupted with different points of view. Should they miss the trail, they could be sent over the falls. Finally a decision was made and they all hoped it was correct. They would stay to the right and listen for the falls.

Rounding the first bend after the campsite they heard the thundering roar and saw the mist ahead. Young Don had been right in his assessment. He knew even in his young age how to read a map as he watched the canoes being rapidly pulled towards the brink. With frantic strokes the teenagers desperately paddled for safety. There was no time to look for the portage. Dave in the bow reefed with all his strength, and they managed to make it to shore. Once safe they hollered to the others and began wading out to help them to safety. The portage on the right was difficult, but they were happy none had been swept over the steep waterfall.

"How are you doing?" Don asked his partner as he lifted the front end of the canoe off the ground. They had loaded their gear inside the canoe and were finding the steep trail a challenge with the added weight.

"I'm ok, but it sure is hot and sticky," came the response.

"We'll be on Achapi Lake soon and find a campsite. Tomorrow's Sunday and we all get a rest."

"Yeah, I sure will be glad of that, but I heard we can't fish or swim," Dave replied. "I sure wish we could."

"Don't you remember? We all agreed to the rules before we started. We would have a real day of rest and have morning services."

"I guess, but I wish we could at least catch a few fish," moaned Dave.

Sunday came and went. Rain, all day, off and on. The tents were soaked but most of the youth were able to get an afternoon nap. The day turned out to be a real day of rest as the leaders kept the entire crew filled with hot pancakes and a few treats while they read and relaxed.

The following day became a day of toil and trouble. Twelve solid hours of paddling, portaging and lining the canoes.

"I think we've gone over twenty miles already," Dave muttered from the bow of the canoe. He was tiring and evening was still a long ways off.

"Hold it, Dave. Do you see the moose on the far shore? I'll take a photo."

"I sure hope your dad's not too upset with the damage to his canoe. The rock we hit today has rippled the canvas and chipped a cedar strip."

"No, my dad knew there might be some damage, and he's cool."

"Look ahead, Dave, this looks like the spot where a portage should be."

"Are you sure, cause most of the canoes are going past us and heading into the white water?"

"No, I believe they are beginning to get out of the canoes and are lining them. Here comes Mr. Collins right behind us."

"We are the only two canoes that are going to portage those rapids," Arnold rasped as he watched the other four canoes struggling through the boulders. "I'm happy we don't have to stumble through that mess of rocks. The river is really fast through here and we could break a leg or flip the canoes over."

Late in the evening the small group of canoes pulled ashore. Abe and Arnold hustled about setting up camp and starting the cooking. Someone had caught two pike and three more pickerel.

"Man alive, I'm starving," murmured Don as he smelled the frying fish. "What a day! I'm so tired I hope I can eat without falling asleep. It's nearly ten o'clock. What a day."

Within a few minutes Abe was dishing out the food and the teenagers began their supper with thoughts of bed and tomorrow's adventures.

Don awoke to the sound of rain. He wondered if they would travel at all today. Finally at 12 p.m. they started down the river. He was glad to be away from the wet soggy campground. The map indicated they would have a seven mile paddle to Eskakwa Falls. Once again he couldn't help thinking of his family at Skookum Lake. They would have been four days there, relaxing, water skiing, swimming, fishing and doing other great things. He shifted his mind back to the task at hand of getting around two big rocks in the middle of the upcoming rapids.

"Smack," the canoe bounced off the one rock and careened into the next one. With a hard reef with his paddle he was able to maneuver half the canoe past the rock when he heard a crunching noise. He was sure it was not a serious hit on the side. No damage.

The next few hours found the group portaging around Upper and Lower Eskakwa Falls and Snake Falls. Back on the river the pair relaxed and began dreaming of supper.

"We're having African dinner tonight," chortled Don, already licking his chops and looking forward to the meal. "Are you as hungry as I am, Dave?"

"What's an African dish?"

"It's one of Mr. Janzen's favourite trip meals: coconut, peanuts, raisins and other goodies on rice. I can't wait."

In a short time they were headed out on Miminiska Lake and looking for a campsite on the south shore.

The rain continued day after day. Depressing for some but Don kept thinking of his family and wondered if it was raining on them. It really did not matter, they always had fun. He thought of the new boat he had just built, an 11'6" stock utility runabout. It replaced his dad's 1948 ten foot boat built many years ago.

Inside the tent he could feel the wild electrical storm raging outside with lightning flashing and thunder roaring as he wrote in his journal.

He knew Tim Janzen was writing a journal as well. They would have some good records of this trip as long as they didn't get them ruined from the rain or soaked in the river.

Finally the rain let up and once again they headed down river.

After navigating several sets of rapids they could see what looked like a dangerous spot ahead.

"Dave, let's maneuver to the other side and miss that V funnel with the rock in the centre," yelled Don.

He watched Abe and Gary in their canoe land on top of a rock in midstream. He gasped in fear as Gary flew up off his seat and became airborne. To his amazement the young man held on and sat back down. Far too close a call, thought Don. The boy came close to being thrown out of the canoe and into the rocks and the strong current where he easily could have perished.

He hoped they could make Lake Petawanga on the morrow with no rain. He was wearing a little thin.

The Miminiska Falls portage wasn't particularly difficult but he began to notice that Janet Foster, one of the two girls on the trip, handled the hard work as well as most of the boys and maybe better than some.

Nancy Gibson was no slouch either. Some perhaps had doubts about girls coming along but not any longer. The next morning found the six canoes stroking north. A light mist hovered over the water as the sun penetrated through, creating a brilliant gem like display of brilliance. The day ahead looked as if it would be dry and without the rain and wind encountered so often.

Unfortunately the first thunderhead appeared in the mid afternoon on Petawanga Lake, and the group headed for shelter on a rocky shoreline. Abe conducted a devotional as they sat under a clear plastic tarp. They had much to be thankful for as there had been no head wind on either Miminiska Lake or Petawanga Lake, which were big lakes. The waves often were high and treacherous during the storms. Abe always said to the teenagers, "God has been good to us." He was truly a man of great faith and true to his calling as a missionary and pastor.

The rain lessened as they moved down Petawanga and near dusk found a suitable campsite on a island. Don felt frustrated as they hit only one rock all day but had damaged the old cedar strip at the bottom of Miminiska Falls. Finally on shore after the tiring day of paddling and portaging, each one took on their responsibilities. "Nine portages so far and eighteen to go. Not a pleasant thought," he muttered to himself.

"I'm making the pudding and the juice tonight," Don mentioned to Gary Leduc.

"Some of us are going fishing, you should come along," Gary said.

" No, all the fish you catch are small. If you catch one over five pounds, I'll eat it raw," Don replied with a chuckle.

Gary and a few of the other boys strolled off along the shoreline casting lures as they went.

Darkness had settled on the camp as the fishing gang arrived back.

"Don, where are you? I have something to show you," Gary's voice could be heard clearly in the evening air.

Don had already gone into his tent to update his journal. With some effort, he climbed out to see what was going on.

"What do you think of that one?" Gary chortled with a grin from ear to ear. "Seven pounds my man. They tell me the Eskimos eat raw fish all the time. When are you going to start eating?"

Several of the fellows were joking and kidding

around. Don could not believe he had trapped himself into this dilemma.

"Give me the fish. I'll fillet it and try eating it," he grumbled, still dazed at the turn of events.

After cleaning and filleting the big fish, he ate a small chunk raw. A few minutes later his stomach began to have a queasy feeling.

Gary and Arnold had been watching, and they agreed he didn't need to eat any more. Don promptly fried up the big slabs so they could eat them in the morning.

The next day around noon they saw some of the villagers waving at them from shore while others were standing watching. They pulled up on dry land to talk to the people. A friendly man told them how they drag the loaded canoes on small rolling logs laid across the path that led around the smaller falls just ahead.

One fellow took time to point out the channels they would need to navigate if they ran the upcoming rapids. "White man said once to me, you must know every rock in the river? I tell dumb white man, no, I only know the channel."

The canoeists made their way down the channel and travelled another few miles before camping for the night.

They awoke to the sound of rain once again in the morning.

Don knew it was Friday and he really looked forward to Sunday and a rest. Finally all the canoes got away at noon and had travelled nearly eight miles when Abe began to yell.

"Head for shore, I'm not sure where we are on the lake."

"I see some guys standing on the shore, let's go talk to them," Arnold suggested as he swung the canoe out.

Harry Baxter had met Abe three years previously. He was standing waiting for the canoes to come ashore. Don had gone to school with Harry's cousin Joe a year before.

After a short, affable discussion, Harry led the group to the narrows, and as they watched he proceeded to take his family down the channel in his new Chestnut canoe. The canoe was a large freighter square back used to transport people and supplies up and down the river.

Don was impressed with how well Harry was able to navigate through the turbulent section without mishap. Wisdom dictated the group of white inexperienced canoeists portage this dangerous section.

The portage proved brutal. Long and hard. No wonder the natives run the river, he thought. Back on the water the group soon encountered rough water once more with massive haystacks. Don and Dave did well working their way through the huge waves and took on only a couple of inches of water. Abe's canoe filled up but they made it safely through. Don was pleased they hadn't hit a rock all day, and he now began to think of rest and washing his hair. It had been a week and his head felt horrible but he could wait one more day. They soon pulled into a good campsite for a well needed rest.

Up early, the paddlers were away by 9 a.m. and kept going till 9 p.m. in the bright sunshine. Although they only had two moderate portages they managed only ten miles due to the constant rapids with three foot high waves. By 9 p.m. they finally found a superb campsite and would spend the next day resting. Don was happy but quite hungry and wondered how the supper meal was going to taste. He watched Abe, busy cooking some kind of soup mixed with oatmeal. Looking on he realized they had been eating Lipton's chicken noodle soup a lot lately and this mixture didn't look appetizing but he would eat it anyway as he was really hungry. Deep down Don wondered if they were running out of food.

The following day was Sunday and provided a well needed day of rest for the whole party. The supper meal the night before had been surprisingly delicious. That was a nice surprise. Finally they all had their first bath in eight days

"Man does that feel good!" Don cried out to Tim Janzen who was swimming past him in the river. Tim was beginning to take on the look of a blond surfer from California who enjoyed the outdoor activities. He was always in good spirits and a lot of fun, which made him a good companion on any adventure. The fact he was blessed with incredible strength helped as well. Tim and Don were of the same age and both destined to be involved in engineering later in life.

The swimming once again reminded Don of the holiday time with his family that he was missing, and he was disappointed in not being able to see his aunt and uncle. His thoughts turned to his brother Barry who had made this same trip three years earlier but could not make this trip. He recalled Barry telling him how they worked all day against a strong headwind on Lake Makokibatan, which was 17 miles long. Abe's group still had nine miles more to go before making camp.

He hoped and prayed their group would have a tailwind as they had finally recovered their energy. A long hard paddle against a strong wind would exhaust them once again.

"Good food, guys, come and get it!" called out Arnold as he began to dish out the bannock and rice supper. "You'll need your strength tomorrow." Don wondered if Arnold knew something he didn't.

Monday morning came and they slept in till 7 a.m. and did not get on the water till nine o'clock. But he was pleased to find the Lord had answered their prayers. They indeed had a tailwind. What a blessing, and by 7 p.m. he knew what Arnold meant the night before. Thirty two long miles of paddling was a good day.

"Wow, we made it to Barry's old campsite on the same day as their group, and we've had low water all the way," sang out Dave.

"Yeah, and we've walked and lined canoes half the way," someone close by commented.

"Life would be a lot easier for me on Skookum Lake, that's for sure," Don quietly mouthed to himself. He couldn't get his family and the lake off his mind. "Two more weeks and I'll be there. I can hardly wait." He looked around to see if anyone heard him.

"Everyone out of bed, you lazy kids," Janet yelled.

"We ought to shoot you! Go back to bed!" He heard someone comment from another tent. Don pried his eyes open and looked at his watch. The time was 5:45 a.m. He was beginning to find each day harder and harder to get up, but he was soon out of the tent. Gord and he were the first ones with their tent packed. He had become accustomed to his tent partner snoring almost every night, which at first had often kept him awake.

Twenty-six miles and three tough portages later they were close to shore when they saw a remarkable sight. A pack of five wolves! Three black and two mousy, grey coloured animals that included two adults and three smaller ones, were running back and forth on the sandy beach.

"Look at the smaller ones playing, they're having fun," whispered Dave.

They had been on Washi Lake for only a few minutes when a strong wind came across the water. The swells increased in size to over three feet and the gang of youngsters loved the surfing effect as they paddled off the crests.

"What a blast, Dave!" Don screamed to his partner over the gale like wind.

As he looked back at the canoes behind him his heart skipped a beat. Terry and young Gord Collins, had run broadside into Abe and Gary Leduc's canoe. Looking back he watched both Abe and Gary fall out of the canoe. As he propelled his own canoe into the next wave he glimpsed back once more.

With a sigh of relief he saw them stand upright in four feet of water as they swayed back and forth holding onto the canoe. Miraculously it had not tipped over and they were now climbing back in.

Thankfully this portion of the lake was shallow as he realized the accident could have been far worse.

"We'd better find a camping spot soon, there's a bad storm brewing on the horizon," Don sang out as he looked to the west.

"You think we should camp on the beach close to the wolves?" Dave yelled back to his partner.

"Nooooo, let's paddle on for a half mile, but hurry."

The clouds had turned black and the wind was blowing

hard as they landed on a sand beach. With only moments to spare they hurriedly put up their tents as a wild and ferocious wind came sweeping down on the them.

With the hurricane wind came a pelting rain as most of them clambered into their tents.

Abe was caught outside and then he saw Don's cedar strip being rolled down the beach, over and over by the extreme wind. He and Gord raced down the beach in pursuit of the craft and finally retrieved the canoe. No serious damage to the craft but the fellows looked like two drenched cats.

Don thanked his chum as he watched him take off his water sogged clothes. The day had been long and he was glad they were done for the day.

The wolves first came while the group sat around the campfire. They wailed mournfully during Abe's devotion time causing irritation among some of the gang. A mixture of yipping and howling set the stage for a long night in the tents.

During the night Don listened as the wolves came close to the tents. With his eyes wide open he heard one sniffing and snorting not far from where he lay. Nervous and a little scared he wished they would go away.

"Gord, are you awake?" No sound came from Gord's sleeping bag and that was strange.

A wolf further down the beach began to howl.

"Gord, how can you sleep through this racket?" Don asked, leaning closer to the other sleeping bag. Still no answer. Then another wolf only a few feet away returned the call. He sat bolt upright with terror in his eyes.

"Go away," he mumbled as he buried his head in his sleeping bag.

The night finally passed and the group carefully exited their tents the next morning. Wolf tracks covered the campsite. The older men prepared breakfast in a short time with rain once more coming down. By noon they finally were packed and were happy to leave the spot to their visitors.

Sixteen miles and eight portages later they decided to camp for the night on a rocky point near the spot where Abe and his partner Ron Swindell had swamped three years previously, which had been a tough moment.

Joe Baxter, the fellow student from the Sault, found them and talked to Abe and Don. He couldn't believe Don was up in the wild country.

Don was sitting on a stump inspecting his feet. They were sore and tender with a huge blister on one foot. He knew he shouldn't go barefoot in the water but he didn't want to get his shoes wet. Some call that teenage logic but walking for now had become extremely difficult. Little did he know things were to get much worse when a huge thorn became imbedded in his foot and became infected. For now he could only dream of going home, which helped keep his mind off the discomfort.

The next day they managed the final two portages, both rough.

"We're finally done the portages," sighed Don as they began the afternoon in the rain but he felt better and his tan was improving.

"Abe says we're only 32 miles from Ogoki."

"I hear we're out of food," Dave said. They were indeed running out of food, and he was hungry. They only had four pancakes and one piece of fish each for breakfast. He wondered how a growing boy could survive on so little. The final portage at Martin Falls and they had a little lunch.

"Yeah, I'm hungry too," said Don, "I hope we have a big pot of something. I'm starved." He looked pensively at the Peterborough canoe hoping it wouldn't need to endure any further abuse.

Forty miles and now past Ogoki. What a day! The water was very low at six inches and the river 400 yards wide, making it hard on all the canoes. They had stopped at the Hudson's Bay Trading Post at Ogoki, which was a mail centre for the area. Don received a half dozen letters and mailed a few to family and friends. Then he bought some cookies with a dollar the Hunter family had sent him.

The store was busy like a beehive, Don thought, but he sort of liked the communal effect after being with the same group for so many days.

Abe had bought some bananas. Don could not believe it! The one thing he hated and could not eat was bananas and now being so hungry he was offered bananas. He had to somehow figure out how to get some food he liked. Don took the bananas anyway and called Gord over.

"Hey Gord, look what I got. Do you want to trade for something?" Don dangled a banana in front of his friend, who loved them.

"What do you want?"

"How about some fig newtons and I'll give you the banana," chirped Don. And so it was that Don ended up with nineteen fig newtons and was proud of his trading skills. Man did they taste good!

The letter from his father had only increased his craving for tarts and seeing his family.

The following two days were the fourth and fifth days without rain. Life was good except they were not eating nearly as well as most of them would have liked. On the Saturday, Don knew his left foot was in bad shape. He had a blister on the ball of his foot and a thorn in his heel. He hoped the river would become deeper so he wouldn't need to help line the canoe. He barely could stand or walk on level ground never mind a stony river bottom.

Don and Dave continued through the shallow rapids and high waves, sometimes zig-zagging from one side of the river to the other. Then at a rest spot Don took a bath and washed his hair and clothes and that felt good.

That night he heard Abe mention they were almost out of food. They already knew that by the rationing for the past few days, but to hear it from Abe was another thing. Their leader was not feeling well tonight and needed rest. Now everyone was concerned, not only about the lack of food but the health of their esteemed leader. They had covered 40 miles today even with a slow down of over an hour repairing a hole in Tom and Phil's canoe.

The boys had punched a hole in the bottom going through a rocky section. Not good. They all agreed they must make better time the next few days before they collapsed from hunger.

One hundred and eighty miles still left to reach Fort Albany. Don wondered if they could make it. Arnold was losing weight quickly but seemed to be strong and resilient. Don wished he felt as good. The family would be heading home from Skookum Lake by now. He knew they would have had a good time.

Sunday, the day of rest, found the group with little food and enduring a morning rain storm. Through the day they watched a native family going up river in a small canoe with a tiny motor that was labouring in the current. They towed another canoe with supplies behind and their dogs ran along the shoreline following them. Don thought they were probably headed for Ogoki. The day was windy and cool, and he was happy they would at least have bannock for supper. The carbohydrate meal would help heat up his body and always tasted great. He still was thinking of butter tarts and dreamed of eating a ton of them when they got back. Sitting in his tent, all he could think of was food and his folks. He couldn't wait to get home.

HEADING FOR THE ALBANY FORKS:

Monday and everyone was paddling hard in hopes of closing the gap to Fort Albany. The food had run out. Don wondered if they could finish the trip without being nourished with good food. What a dilemma! They all prayed hard last night and this morning, that somehow they would find someone who might sell them food. Besides no food, they were losing blood. The mosquitoes had become intolerable, unbelievably thick, far worse than in his hometown of the Soo far to the south.

And then came the answer to prayer. From out of nowhere, an Native man came out to talk to them. To the teenagers, God became far more real as the fellow produced a fourteen pound sturgeon. Abe gave him ten dollars for it and everyone became brighter.

Suddenly the day changed with the sun shining and a good meal to look forward to. Don was in pain through the day from his infected heel and could no longer put his weight on it. He was so happy they had no more portages or canoe lining. Things could be worse.

Fifty miles later they ended the long day of paddling and pulled ashore for their well deserved rest and anticipated meal and a good night's sleep.

HAT ISLAND:

The next day was extremely difficult, first in the drizzle in the morning and then rain in the afternoon. Don had found the sturgeon good, but then as hungry as he was maybe anything would taste good. Unfortunately several of the crew became sick but they paddled on. He wondered if they ate too much and their citified stomachs couldn't handle the strong meat or maybe the fish was not cooked enough. He was glad it hadn't affected him.

"Dave, look over to the right. Isn't that a bear?" Don asked his partner.

"Sure is and I'm glad we're in the centre of the river. He might be as hungry as we are," Dave laughed.

"Speaking of that, if I had a gun I'd shoot it so we could eat it," came the reply. "Someone once told me bear meat can be reeeaally really tasty if it's cooked properly." Don could hear his friend chuckling in the bow. At least someone could find humour even when not feeling well.

Forty miles and they made Hat Island. The group would stay the night and travel on to Black Bear Island the next day some 42 miles away.

Dave and Don were told today they were pushing too hard. The boys were always racing far ahead in an endeavour to make time. At one point they had to wait for an hour and a half for others to catch up.

"I just want to make it to the Fort without missing too many meals," Don commented as he watched a pair of Canada geese land in the water. "Boy, I wish I could catch one of those guys. I bet they would taste yummy."

Paddling through a storm with thunder and lightning, his mind began to wander into things like what his folks were eating for supper and how many of his mom's butter tarts he could eat.

"I plan to eat so much when I get home I won't be able to walk," he mumbled under his breath.

"Did you say something?" Dave yelled back to him. "I can't hear a thing in this driving rain."

"No, just dreaming."

There was no longer any thought of stopping to get out of the rain. They surged on and completed another 43 miles. Tired, dirty and hungry they came upon a couple of folks from Ottawa who kindly gave them some milk and flour for making bannock. They would eat tonight.

Two days left to completion. The next day was sunny as the gang hit the water at 9 a.m. but the wind came up and they had to paddle through four foot waves. Finally they pulled in at 3:30 p.m. after covering a mere 23 miles. They were only doing two miles an hour in the strong wind and huge waves. Supper consisted of one fig cookie, one piece of toast and two scoops of pudding. The teenagers seemed satisfied as they still had a little tea and coffee left, which tasted good.

THE FINAL DAY ON THE WATER:

Don awoke the next morning and crawled out the front opening. The air was cool and as he unzipped the screen he noticed frost had formed in various areas. Shivering a little he pulled on a sweater and stood up.

After a short time around the fire and a little tea for breakfast, they prepared to leave on their final push.

What a feeling, realizing they would be at Fort Albany today as they pulled away from the campsite, a little hungry and looking forward to filling their stomachs with lots of food.

Then came the big haystacks. Four foot haystacks, but the travellers were well seasoned by now in the art of controlling their craft through the mighty waves. Even so, Don and Dave's canoe filled up with water. One of the few times on the trip but it was exciting and they loved it. Arnold was taking pictures and the boys hoped he would preserve them for posterity. Maybe they'd be in the movies someday.

At last they arrived at Fort Albany, and the teens ran for the Hudson's Bay store. Don purchased a number of chocolate bars and devoured five of them, one after the other.

The chief of the village, a friendly helpful man, came with his truck and took them to the runway. A DC-3 came roaring out of the sky a scant 20 minutes later. They had thought it would be two days before they could fly out but here they were stacking the canoes one on top of the other in the cargo hold of the plane and preparing to fly out immediately.

Abe's voice could be heard over the loud din of the hustle and bustle of the teens. "Put Elliot's canoe on the top of the other canoes so it doesn't get damaged." Most of them were either fiberglass or aluminum and in poor condition and he knew how important the Peterborough was to Don and his dad. He did not want it damaged any more than it already was.

A short time later the plane was flying above the flat

land and lakes heading for the town of Moosonee and on to Timmins.

EPILOGUE:

A short ending to a long and tough trip for the teenagers but one final story. On the way home Don was laying on the floor in the back of the big van dozing when he felt the vehicle stop and he thought they must be in Kenagami but didn't bother to open his eyes. And then suddenly *heaven came down* to a 15 year old. He came awake with butter tarts flying through the air all around him.

"Elliot, here's your butter tarts you've been whining about for so long." Arnold had found two packs of butter tarts in the store, and after listening to Don for nearly half the trip wishing for some, he rushed them out to the young lad. Oh, the feeling when a craving is fulfilled. Arnold instantly became a hero in Don's eyes. Later that week his mother made more for him and he devoured 72 of them in a short time.

In the end all turned out well with kudos to the two adult leaders Abe and Arnold who brought the team home safely. A lot of responsibility with a group of teens but these leaders had trusted in God to bring them all back safely. They had their struggles and ups and downs and we can understand only in part how the younger members felt through the trip. The long days of rain, and the day after day of arm weary paddling would have increased their desire to get the trip over but they kept their spirits high and finished well. And so we end a great story of exhilaration, trial and adventure with each one having the satisfaction of completing a 500 mile trip down a wilderness river and a lifetime of memories.

Rick and Chico

4. TROUBLED WATERS

There have been strange tales told from years past of most unusual happenings in the northern wilderness. Following is a story that may give you reason to reconsider your next trip to the great outdoors.

Rick depressed the gas pedal on the old panel truck as it laboured up the steep hill at Montreal River harbour. He gazed out the side window at the big lake on his left noting that small waves had begun to form. This was a concern as it was very early in the morning and the winds usually increased as the day wore on. They still had an hour of driving to make it to Old Woman Bay where they planned to launch their fishing boat from the beach. From there they would head down the shore of Lake Superior to Bushy Bay several miles to the south. Should the wind increase, the waves would be higher and trying to get out on the water from the beach would be more difficult. The wind was usually stronger during late August and would make a trip along the Lake Superior shoreline somewhat precarious.

He kept an eye on the road ahead watching for moose. They often came up on the highway hoping to cross. Close to forty of the big animals were killed each year on this remote stretch between the city of Sault Ste. Marie and the town of Wawa. He only hoped they saw the moose and could stop in time. He was determined to stay vigilant.

Perched on top of the old truck was a fourteen foot fishing boat and a small Grumman canoe lashed down tightly with nylon ropes.

Rick took his eyes off the road for a moment and took a quick glimpse at his friend on the opposite seat. Chico, his long time friend, was dressed in a faded rain jacket and striped jogging pants. He sat upright, intently looking out the front window watching for moose.

"What do you think about those clouds?" Rick asked, waving his arm to the northeast. He wore a faded jean jacket and pants and wore dark shades. He hadn't shaved this morning. The day old stubble and black hair gave him a fierce look similar to the great Mongolian warriors of centuries past.

"Let's hope they keep heading east," Chico responded. "We're going to have a hard time getting out on the water by the look of those waves." Generally more careful than his friend in tenuous situations he would often suggest alternate ways of doing things, making him a valuable asset on any outing. His big smile and friendly personality made it easy for others to like him.

A short time later they passed the park sign and Kinney Lake on the east side of the highway. The men often took a quick glance at the small lakes that appeared close to the road as they moved further inland from Lake Superior.

Both remained quiet as their thoughts recalled the many trips to the park interior in years past. This morning the memories increased their desire to be on the water and heading for a new adventure.

In less than an hour they were pulling into the parking lot of Old Woman Bay. A stiff breeze had continued to develop and they could see what looked like two foot waves crashing onto the sand beach.

"Let's get a move on, Chico, the wind is only going to get worse," Rick sang out as he stepped from the vehicle.

The pair quickly undid the ropes and deposited the boat and canoe on the shoreline, with the motor, oars and paddles. Throwing in their two packsacks and gear, they began the strenuous job of getting out on the water. Pushing and pulling the two men struggled through the waves with the bouncing boat, until Rick was able to jump in. Meanwhile Chico was having trouble tying the canoe on behind as it flopped up and down. The waves washed over him as he finally completed the job and then with his clothes thoroughly soaked he managed to crawl over the gunwales and fall into the boat.

Without delay he grabbed the oars and rowed feverishly into the wind. Rick pulled on the starter cord of the ancient eighteen horse outboard, wishing they had a larger motor, but it was all they could find to use on this trip.

The outboard suddenly coughed and then died. Rick said a silent prayer and reefed once more on the cord. The old engine came to life and as he throttled it down he put it in gear. Straightening out the boat and facing it south they cut through the waves.

Looking back towards the shore, Chico saw a man standing on the beach waving at them. He seemed to be yelling and pointing down the lake.

"Richard! Richard! Look behind you! Someone is waving and yelling at us."

"I can't hear you over this motor, what is it?" he bellowed into the wind. He didn't know what his friend was trying to tell him.

Chico leaned forward close to Rick's ear. "There was a man with white hair standing on the beach trying to tell us something."

Rick shrugged his shoulders. "We can't turn around now, it's too late. The water is getting rougher and we have a long way to go."

Chico slid back on the middle seat, as his face masked an unanswered question. Who was the man back on the beach and what was he trying to tell them?

For the moment all that really mattered was that Rick steer clear of any rocks close to the surface and stay a good distance from the shore. Black boulders of all sizes lined the edges, seemingly forever. At first the big rocks tumbled one on top of the other, but as the boat moved forward they began to grow in height and soon became sheer cliffs. They glistened in the sun, black and frightening. No place to land safely and with the wind growing in intensity they stayed far from shore.

The first mile went by with the bow of the boat thumping through the waves, taking all Rick's concentration to keep the boat angled out into the lake. The ride was rough and as they neared the first big point the wind seemed to increase and the waves became higher.

Chico began to bail out the water that came splashing over the side. He was glad he had worn his rain jacket or he'd be saturated again. He had begun to dry out from the first soaking and was finally feeling somewhat warmer.

The cliffs continued to rise higher as they progressed down the big lake, hoping they could see the spot to land where the trail to the inland lake began.

Chico faced the back of the boat and kept his eyes on the canoe that trailed behind. The craft was built of light aluminum, and he hoped the repeated thudding from the waves wouldn't do any damage. He thought of their friend John and was glad the man wasn't here to see his canoe being battered like this. They had borrowed it because it only weighed forty pounds and they had to carry it a fair distance through the bush. Rick and he had asked their friend to come on the trip but for some unexplained reason he had declined. They had been on numerous trips over the years and always enjoyed the challenge but this time John had given them a strange look and wished them a safe journey.

Chico was brought abruptly out of his thoughts by the sound of a loud voice. "Hey Bud! Let's bring that canoe into the boat before it gets wrecked," Rick yelled over the roar of the outboard.

They slowed the boat down and managed to pull the canoe alongside and hoist it over the centre thwart. Chico kept it balanced with a firm grip. He began to wonder why they would even attempt this trip with these high waves. Rick carefully watched ahead hoping to avoid rocks under the surface that would potentially destroy their propeller.

The miles went by and the waves grew in intensity but the high cliffs eventually dropped off and a small pebble beach appeared from nowhere. The wind pushed the boat too far past and they had to come back around a small point of land. Pulling up on the beach they carefully looked along the brush and located an overgrown trail leading away from the big water. Rick looked south, his eyes following the shoreline that was covered with huge boulders. He thought he saw movement among the rocks but then it was gone. Perhaps an animal, but it looked tall and thin.

The pair emptied the boat and secured it, then took their packsacks, paddles and canoe and headed for the dim trail that led inland.

After the first long carry, Rick stopped and lifted the aluminum canoe off his shoulders and placed it carefully on the ground. They had been walking on the hard to follow trail that had several deadfalls and although it was on a continual rise, they encountered boggy areas that forced both him and Chico to step carefully along the sides. In other places the winter snows had pushed the tag alders completely over the path causing them to circumvent the blocked trail by crashing through the brush.

Glad to be relieved of the weight he sat down on one of the canoe seats and kept an eye on his chum who had stopped a few feet ahead. The day was warming up and sweat ran down his forehead into his eyes and under his grizzled chin. Chico came back and sat on a clump of dry ground and let his pack slide off his back. His well tanned face glistened from the perspiration and he welcomed the rest. He sat staring at the canoe in front of him.

"That canoe has been to a lot of lakes in this park," he said, almost to himself as to his friend.

"Yeah, remember Old Woman Lake and all those ponds and Woodpecker and some of the lakes past it," Rick replied.

Chico had closed his eyes and seemed on the verge of dreamland.

"Come on bud, let's keep moving, we should be halfway there," Rick sang out as he hoisted the canoe back up on his shoulders.

Occasionally a mosquito would land on his bare skin and attempt to make a feast from the human blood. Small flies often flew in their face causing the men to cough or rub their eyes vigorously. They were thankful the season was summer and not spring or the bug situation would be intolerable.

Chico had moved well ahead when he slowed to a crawl. The air had become hot and oppressive and he was sweating so much his shirt was soaked. They were entering a strange and formidable looking part of the trail, somewhat reminiscent of pictures he had seen from the jungles of the Amazon. The overhanging trees had grown in such way they hung close to the trail and blocked out the sun. The vegetation had even changed. Throughout the entire area the ferns and weeds had grown tall and willowy making the walking difficult. Even the way the long stemmed plants grew with their broad leaves was much different from the normal growth he was accustomed to. He looked back at his friend.

"Careful, Rick, this long grass can cut your hands and it's hard to see your feet."

"Look out!" he yelled, as he crashed to the ground with the paddles and the rest of the gear.

He lay for a moment thinking what kind of strange, scary place this was, here in the Cambrian Shield. A place so different he could almost envision the dark hidden paths that led through the dense forests of South America and thought

75

of the first explorers as they slashed their way through with their machetes, sweating and muttering about the heat. Even the smell was unlike any other he had ever encountered.

Rick had walked up to him and stood close by with the canoe still on his shoulders. He watched Chico stand, readjust his pack and begin to move forward, working his way slowly through the long strands of grass. Rick was glad the two of them had the stamina to make this trip in the heat. He wondered how many years he had left to endure this kind of torture.

A stiff breeze blew across the lake, causing the man in the sling chair to turn sideways. John sat on the beach on the property he and his wife had recently purchased. He sat contemplating the reason he was here this weekend when he could be exploring and fishing a remote lake in Lake Superior Park.

A tiny stream ran past a small cabin on a knoll behind him. This was the reason he had given up a weekend in the remote wilds in order to continue their new hobby of enlarging the original building and putting on new wood siding. Full well he knew there was a multitude of other construction projects.

He recalled someone saying that "camp," as cottages in the north are called, is spelled "work." What had he done in agreeing to buy this place? Without question they would be working here for many, many years. Granted, they sat on a semi-remote lake that had reasonably good lake trout and bass fishing but even so his heart was in exploring new areas and finding new lakes.

His thoughts returned to where he might be if he was with his two chums in the park. He could almost envision them portaging into the fabled trout lake and the sweet eagerness of how good the fishing was going to be and how restful a spot it would be.

A loud noise from the cabin woke him from his wanderings and he heard his wife calling him to lunch. He knew once lunch was over they both would be back to work, hoping to fulfill their dream of making the old camp into a larger dwelling, with bright pine cove siding and a new big porch.

He remained seated as he wondered how the boys were doing. He found himself somewhat ill at ease. Something was grating on his conscience but he couldn't nail it down. Perhaps they had run into some kind of trouble or maybe things hadn't happened yet. He wished again he had gone but he had never liked fishing out of a small canoe with three people and with his wife wanting to keep working on the camp, the decision not to go was relatively easy. At least till now. Some concerns he couldn't explain had began to invade his thoughts, and he was beginning to worry and that was something he knew was useless.

John lifted himself from his seat and made his way to the small porch where his wife had laid out lunch.

"Thanks love. I am really hungry," he said as he sat down on a small lawn chair. He looked solemnly at the table and the food and glass of juice before him.

His wife Mary looked over at him before responding. "You seem to be in another world this morning, hon. What's going on inside that head of yours?"

"Ah, I've been thinking about our two friends out there in Lake Superior in a little boat going down the shoreline. Bad things can happen if the wind gets up, or they could get hurt while they're miles in the park."

"They'll be alright," came the quick response. "They're still young and strong and reasonably careful."

"Yea, you think so. Don't believe it. They can do dumb things like everyone else," he replied.

"They'll be fine, quit worrying. Anyway, what do you always tell me we should do in times like these?"

"Yes of course, pray. You're right, that's all I can do today sitting here. Why do I have to be reminded that God's the one in control of all things. Let's ask our Heavenly Father to watch over and protect those two characters." John took a moment to bow his head and give thanks for the food and then asked God to keep his two buddies safe.

After lunch John picked up his tool belt and headed for the small lumber pile. Back to work, but his mind still was being invaded by some unknown force that left him thinking of his two friends and the dangers he sensed they could be in.

The wind was sweeping through the tops of the trees as the two men continued their trek along the dim trail.

"We will have to be sure we're on the big lake early in the day when we return or we could be into another big wind," croaked Chico as he came to a stop and laid the equipment he had been carrying on the ground.

"Listen to that wind howl," Rick replied looking up at the spruce trees swaying from side to side. "The wind always seems to get worse in the afternoon along Lake Superior for some reason."

"Crack"—a noise came from behind them, somewhere in the bush. Then silence as the two stood still and listened.

"Wonder what made that noise?" Rick asked as he watched the back trail.

"Probably an old tree being blown over from the big wind," Chico replied. "I see water ahead, Rick. I hope that's Gravel Lake."

"Yeah, it will be and that means we'll soon be at the old campsite on Chaillon Lake, old buddy," came a tired voice from beneath the canoe.

The two men paddled across the small body of water called Gravel Lake on the map and then carried the canoe and gear over the short portage to a desolate campsite that sat high above the waters of Chaillon Lake. Long grass grew in patches throughout the level clearing with a large number of scraggy bushes growing in the sandy areas.

"We have some brushing to do before we can set up our tent," mumbled Chico looking over the spot.

Rick was staring down the lake, hoping to see some activity on the water. A substantial wind from the southwest was sending small waves against the rocks below. He would have to wait for the wind to rescind before he'd be able to see a fish jump or see bugs on the surface. As he prepared to carry the canoe down to the shore, he turned and happened to glance down the lake where another campsite was situated near the Red Rock River. They had seen no one on the lake but he was sure he had seen movement in that direction. Walking over to his pack, he located a small set of binoculars and began scanning the east side of the lake. He could see no tent or human activity. Strange, he thought, maybe his eyes were playing tricks on him.

The next couple of hours found the men cleaning up the old campsite and setting up their tent. They kept busy preparing to go out on the lake for some fishing. That was the reason they were here, to catch and eat fish. They knew there were three species of fish in this lake. In the past spring with their chums they had fished and caught rainbow, lake, and brook trout. Now that was a trip indeed, Chico reminisced as he sat on a stump talking to his friend. The trip had involved two hard days of tripping and seven days on the lake. He recalled how his chum Rick had begun the trip with a bad cold and still was able to carry a sixty pound canoe and a sixty pound pack over several long difficult portages. He remembered the steepness of the Surf Lake hill and how long the final leg of the journey felt, carrying all their gear for two miles down an aged logging road. And then a day later, they had watched their friend sit in an old wooden chair at the campsite in a daze and wondered how he had been able to keep going in his weakened condition.

"Yes, I thought I was going to die that day sitting on the chair. I felt so weak," Rick replied as he listened to Chico retell the story.

"I'll tell you, Rick, we were all worried you might catch pneumonia and pass on. That day had started with rain and cold. Remember pulling the canoes over the big snow drift at the end of Connel Lake? Johnny and I had trained for the trip for weeks and we were strong and ready. Our canoe only weighed forty pounds and we took turns carrying it but you opted to carry your own canoe over all the portages. Somehow you managed and lived through it, even sick as you were."

"Come on, bud, let's get out on the water and catch some of those monster trout," Rick barked as he took his fishing pole and headed down the slope to the waiting canoe. He had enough recalling of that day.

The evening had arrived and they fished till near dark. They were alone on the lake, and as they paddled slowly forward they could see the signs of early autumn as the trees were beginning to turn colour. Arriving back at the campsite they had time for a quick meal and to gather a pile of branches for the night fire.

Later as they sat staring at the blazing logs they heard the lonesome call of a wolf from the far end of the lake that sent shivers up their spine. Then a few more of the pack joined in and made a chorus that would worry the biggest moose within hearing distance. The men looked at each other nervously and stared into the darkness.

"I'm heading for the sack," Chico muttered as he rose from his seat. He hoped the smell of the two fish they had cleaned and eaten didn't attract the wolf pack.

The pair of fishermen soon fell asleep with the smell of fresh fried trout lingering in their noses.

Two hours later Chico sat bolt upright as he heard the end of another long lonely wail of a wolf. The sound seemed to come only a short distance from the campsite.

"Great, there's wolves out there and I have to go out to get rid of that tea I drank," he murmured under his breath. He looked over at his sleeping chum who was snoozing quietly away. "Yeah, lucky guy, he never has to go out in the night."

Chico unzipped the tent door and stepped out into the cool night air. All was quiet. He peered into the dark bush surrounding the campsite and could see no movement. A comforting thought came to him as he stood at the edge of the clearing. He had often heard that wolves stay away from human scent and had never been known to kill a human being. Nonetheless, he wished he had a gun of some sort for protection, but that was not allowed in Canada.

He had just finished getting rid of the tea when he heard a distinct thump less than a hundred feet in the dense brush. He froze and looked towards the sound. Wolves don't make thumping noises in the night. What could that be? Slowly he began edging back to the tent. And then came a sharp sound as if a small branch had been stepped on and broken.

"Ok, I can't let the sounds of the night bother me like that." He entered the tent and hoped whatever had made the heavy thump was not a bear looking for food.

Chico lay with his eyes open as he listened for a long time for more noises. Finally he slept.

The first glimmer of light began to brighten the inside of the tent as the dawn broke over the forested wilderness.

The two fishermen climbed out to meet the new bright day. They scrounged around and found some smaller twigs on the ground and in a few minutes Rick had a fire blazing using birch bark he had peeled from a nearby tree. He threw on larger branches and proceeded to put water in a metal can and hang it over the fire from a green pole.

Looking down the lake he could see very little as a dense fog had settled over the water during the night.

"Let's get out on the lake and catch some of those fish, chum," Rick said as he poked away at the burning twigs waiting for the water to boil.

"Alright, but I need a hot drink and a granola bar," his partner replied. "Hey Sleeping Beauty, did you hear any noises outside the tent last night?"

"No, I never woke up at all."

"Well, I did when I went out but have no idea what it was. I heard something heavy hitting the ground."

Some time later the pair climbed into the canoe and began to fish the upper bay close to their camp. The sun had risen and dispelled most of the fog and now they were able to see nearly all the way to the end of the lake. Turning the canoe southward they began a slow troll along one shoreline. Rick was still intrigued by what he thought was movement on the eastern shoreline at dusk the night before.

Now as he strained to see through the lifting fog he once again was sure he could see something standing on the far shore. To him it appeared to be a giant human. Perhaps the form was simply a tall stump or the remains of a dead tree.

"Chico, do you see what I see down the lake on the south end?"

Chico looked intensely in the direction Rick was pointing. The sun was bright where they sat on the lake but a few hundred yards further on the fog made it difficult to be sure what they were looking at. How well they knew how mist and fog could play tricks on the eyes and make one think you saw things that were something else.

"Yeah, I think I see what you think you see. Let's wait and see if it moves but let's head down there," he responded.

Rick continued to paddle and kept his eye on the gigantic form outlined on the shore. Suddenly his rod whipped backwards and he frantically grabbed it to keep it from flying out of the canoe. "Fish on! Fish on!" he yelled and began to furiously reel his line in. His "Ugly Stick" that he had purchased a couple of years before was bent double. This was one big fish as his fishing rod was not wimpy and took a lot of weight.

Chico had turned in the bow seat and found the net on the floor, but could not move it. Rick had his big boot on it.

"Steady, Rick, slow down and set the hook hard." He sang out. His partner didn't hear a word. He was totally engrossed in the ongoing battle.

"Rick! Rick! Lift your foot, I can't get the net!" screamed Chico as he tried lifting the net off the floor. Well did he know how upset his chum would be if he was unable to net this big one.

The big fish jumped far in the air. Now they could see it was a huge rainbow. The battle was electrifying as the fish was brought closer to the canoe. The fish suddenly leaped once more, allowing the men to see its brilliant silver sides and watch it shake its mighty head from side to side. They were amazed and mesmerized to witness the acrobatics put on by this fine specimen. And then without warning came the disappointment and the letdown as the fish spit out the lure. They watched a big blue "Cleo" sail majestically through the air and fall into the water. The great fish was gone.

Rick was emotionally spent. Indeed it had been only a few moments of a battle with the largest fish he had ever hooked. The thrill had been fantastic but the disappointment was deeply bitter. He could only stare ahead in stunned silence with a blank look.

Chico was still trying to pull the net from under Rick's foot and wondered how things would have turned out when the fish came alongside and Rick yelling at him to net it and he couldn't get the net free. How mad would Rick be if they had lost the fish. Well, he would never know.

The two men began to slowly paddle again. Never more were those famous words from the Olympics so true, "The thrill of victory and the agony of defeat." The big fish had won. Someone, somewhere was clapping but Rick knew what they meant by the agony of defeat.

Chico had turned forward in his seat and was looking down the lake. The far shoreline was clear and they had drifted much closer. "I don't see anything on the shore, Rick."

"Me either," Rick responded. "But I am sure I saw something. Maybe my eyes are playing tricks on me but I don't think so. Let's go ashore and look around."

They made their way into the far bay and landed on the desolate beach. As they walked about stretching their legs, Rick swept his eyes over the sandy area and along the long grass where it grew close to the bush. He could see signs of travel, presumably made by wildlife, some smaller prints of animals but no human prints. Then he saw what looked like a massive footprint in the sand. As far as he could tell it looked fresh. Whoever had made the print could not be human as it was some twenty inches in length and ten inches wide.

"Chico, look at this and tell me what you think?" he yelled.

Chico walked over to where Rick stood and gazed down at what appeared to be a large print of a human bare foot. He cast his eyes about on the small beach and could see other signs that would indicate activity of some sort that were at least a week old.

"What do you imagine made that?" Rick looked at his friend, hoping for extra insight into what he thought he saw.

"Well, I think probably somebody walked barefoot here awhile ago and the rain spread the footprint, making it look bigger," replied Chico. To him that was the only rational answer. He didn't believe in the "Sasquatch" stories or the "Windigo" folklore you often heard about on television.

Rick walked to the edge of the clearing and examined the tall grass and tag alders that were well trampled down.

"Perhaps," he replied, "but something big went through this bush."

"I'm sure moose come out here often for a drink. These other marks on the beach could be anything. Let's go," his friend said, turning to go.

They began to walk back to the canoe when Rick held up his hand. "Do you smell something strange?"

"I smelled it when we came ashore. It's probably some kind of wild flower."

Rick took one last look around and then shoved the canoe out into the water. With soft easy strokes the two fishermen headed out into the bay, hoping to pick up a couple of fish for supper.

A few hours later the tired men arrived back at their camp and pulled their canoe up on the rocky shore.

"Let's get these fish cleaned and have a nap before supper," Rick said. He always looked forward to a little rest time in the mid afternoon. That was an enjoyable part of every trip for him.

After the quick process of gutting the three lakers they had caught, they climbed up the small incline to where their tent sat.

"What happened here?" Rick cried out as he looked at the tent, which was half down. The back pole had been pulled out with several of the ground stakes scattered about.

"I'd say we had a visitor, but I wonder who or what kind?" Chico replied with a look of disgust on his face.

Rick walked around the tent and then headed over to the packs that were hung six feet off the ground on an old birch tree. "I don't think it was a bear, it would have ripped these packs to shreds to get at the food inside them."

Chico was walking around the rest of the campsite trying to find telltale signs of the intruder. The only other visible change they could see was the water can had been flung across the clearing and the frying pan now lay in a different area. Then he saw toe prints or at least what he thought were big toe marks.

"Rick, come here and look at this. Something left a half a footprint with six toes."

"There we go again, this wasn't 'Bigfoot' or something strange, bud," Rick replied as he sauntered over to look at the marks. "All we know for sure was that some animal came in and nosed around, probably a wolf or something. Let's fix this tent and have a rest."

Chico shrugged but looked nervously along the encroaching brush nearest the tent. Strange things had happened in the wilds before, like rabbits tripping on tent poles in the night and bouncing off his leg that lay against the inside of the tent. He'd heard of many strange things but his only real concern was if a bear was nearby. Then they would have to go home. He was tired and needed some rest.

The inside of the tent was warm as one of the last days of summertime was coming to a close. Rick snoozed peacefully on top of his sleeping bag while his friend lay awake looking out the tent door. Chico could see the clear blue water that stretched southward and could see long dark shadows stretching far out in the lake formed by the tall trees that grew near the shore. An hour passed, and he knew they needed to be out on the water if they were going to do any fishing before dark.

"Come on, fella, let's get out there," he mumbled as he climbed out the tent opening. Some horseflies buzzed close by and he could see a large dragonfly perched on a rock at the campfire. A peaceful setting and he was tempted to forget the fishing and go back in and have another nap.

At that moment Rick appeared, refreshed and eager to be on the water. Grabbing a bag of mixed nuts and berries and a bottled drink, he hurried across the opening and down to the canoe.

"I hope whatever came here earlier doesn't come back," his chum bellowed down to him; his energy had rebounded.

"Naw, whatever it was is gone," came the reply.

Chico had begun to have a feeling of impending doom, perhaps only a little worry that some wild animal could wreck their weekend. For now he would concentrate on catching one of those big rainbows that cruised under the canoe.

The lake was still, with only a whisper of wind coming from the southwest. The men trolled their lines behind the canoe and paddled softly fifty yards off shore, each one deep in his own thoughts. The stillness of the approaching night only helped amplify an occasional sound from the forest. With darkness approaching they hoped for some action from below before heading in. An hour or so passed and the trees had turned a dark colour of green. The warmth of the day began to fade as a chill came over the water with a mist beginning to settle over the lake. The paddlers turned the canoe for home.

Rick sat upright and listened. He had heard a distinct sound, coming from down the lake. Chico turned and looked at him with a look of wonder in his eyes. "Did you hear that?"

"Shhhush." Rick held up a hand for silence. Then they heard clearly a sweet, melodious tune coming softly across the water.

"Chico, that's sounds like a flute or piccolo."

"Isn't that weird, there's no one else on the lake. Where is that coming from, I wonder?" his friend sat dead still as if transfixed by the music.

The sound seemed to envelop them as they listened. Then as quickly as it came it left, leaving the pair of men to ponder on what they had just heard.

"You know Chico, our friend John told me of one time he and his wife heard the same thing on a lake that had no humans on it. We'll talk to him about that when we get back."

Darkness was settling in as the men arrived back at camp. Rick stood atop the small rise and peered down the lake still wondering what they thought they had heard. Chico walked up to him and was about to tell him he would get a fire going when he saw movement once more in one of the far bays. A shadowy form could be seen rushing through the settling mist. Whatever it was appeared to be colossal. This time both men felt a tinge of trepidation.

"That's no bear, and it sure doesn't look like any moose to me," Chico broke the silence. "I'm sure it had two legs."

They stood for a long time waiting for whatever they had seen to reappear. A moon had risen but darkness still obscured the far end and they were unable to see anything. The men shrugged and without a word turned to build a fire and boil water for their dinner. Sitting around the campfire was reassuring as they watched the flying sparks float away into the night air. Strange things had been known to happen in isolated areas of the bush before, and tonight the normal peaceful spirit of the lake had been broken by the unknown. They spoke little, which was unusual as they often discoursed on many subjects like skiing, tennis, fishing and family. Tonight was different; the fishing had not been great and they had begun to wonder about some of the things they had seen and heard throughout the day.

"Let's go home tomorrow," Rick suggested as he took one last swig from his mug of hot tea. "The fishing's not too good and I have work I can be doing."

"Sure," came the reply, "but let's fish for a couple of hours in the morning. We're bound to catch something."

"I'm turning in," replied his partner as he headed for the tent.

Chico lay in his sleeping bag with his eyes open. The smell of the burnt embers reached his nostrils but with it came a sweet strange aroma. He surmised the smell must be from the crushed weeds or grass near the tent. The night was silent when from behind the tent came a noise. "Thump, thump!"

"Rick, are you awake?" Chico whispered.

"Yeah, I heard it. What is that?"

"That's the same sound I heard last night."

And then again came the thumping sound as if someone was jumping on the ground.

"Go on! Get out of here!" Rick bellowed loudly. The two men lay listening, hoping the noise wasn't from a bear.

"Go back to sleep, Chico. Who knows what that was."

"I have to go out."

"What do you want me do, hold your hand?" came the reply from deep within Rick's sleeping bag.

"Smart guy eh! If I don't come back you can explain it to my family," Chico barked and exited the tent.

Through the rest of the night the pair awoke occasionally but they heard no more strange noises.

The morning arrived with the usual mist over the water. They knew the day would be sunny as they watched the rays of sunlight streaking through the tops of the tallest trees. A breeze had come up, which was not the best sign for their return trip out on Lake Superior.

After a fast breakfast of granola bars and raisins washed down with Gatorade the men walked down to the canoe and looked out over the water watching the fog.

"Maybe we should head back before the wind

91

becomes too strong," Chico said, almost to himself. A shiver went down his back. He definitely felt weird.

"Yeah, let's go," replied Rick as he scanned the distant shoreline with his small set of binoculars. Once more he believed he detected movement in the far bay. As he watched he was sure he saw a tall, two legged something moving along the beach.

"Here Chico, take a look at this," he handed the binoculars to his friend.

Chico took a minute to focus the eye pieces. "Whoa. What's that?" he exclaimed trying to get a better view. He felt the distance was too great to define what he thought he saw and wished they had stronger glasses.

"Well, I'm unable to make out what that is, but we don't have time to go down there, and even if we did I'm not sure I'd want to. You hear that wind? It's getting stronger. Let's go now."

The two men began to strike camp and pack their sleeping bags away and take down the tent. In less than an hour they had tied up their gear and then stood for one last look at the empty clearing where they had stayed.

As they entered the first portage to Gravel Lake, Rick could hear a long moaning sound coming from deep in the forest. He marvelled at the idea there might be something strange inhabiting this part of the wilderness. How easily one could get caught up in the fantasies of the mind and of things that were unexplainable. An element of fear had begun to invade his thoughts because of the unknown sights and sounds they had encountered during the trip.

He should have been far more concerned of what lay ahead on the big waters of Kitchegoomee if only he had been able to see into the future.

The morning was warm and the sky clear as the men moved down the long trail west of Gravel Lake. Once again they worked their way through the area with the tall grass with the large broadleaves and the strange vegetation that resembled the dense growth in the countries far to the south. The sun was high in the sky as the men pushed their way towards the shores of Superior.

"I think I see blue sky not far ahead," Chico sang out. They had taken several rests along the way and now the day was getting hot.

A short time later Rick took the canoe from his tired shoulders and placed it softly on the small rocks that lined the shore of the big lake.

"Here we are, and it looks like the wind's not too bad. We should be able to handle that small chop on the water."

"Yeah, I guess we got here early enough to miss the big afternoon winds," his partner replied.

Loading their gear in the boat, they lifted it off the rocks and into the water and tied the canoe on behind. Pushing off shore a short distance Rick pulled the rip cord on the motor. After several pulls and a silent prayer the engine sparked and then idled without a miss.

"Everything's going great so far," Chico shouted over the roar of the engine. "The boat and motor were here and the motor started and there's very little wind. We should be able to blast back to the beach in no time."

Rick put the eighteen horse motor into gear and headed towards a point of land not far in the distance.

The small chop when they began soon materialized into a two foot wave less than a mile down the lake. The wind increased quickly and Rick had to stay attentive to keep the boat angled into the rising swells.

He knew he must stay a good distance from shore as there were submerged rocks under the water which he would never see in time to avoid tearing the bottom end out of the motor.

Chico pulled the canoe up to the side of the boat and pulled it lengthwise into the interior.

The waves began to increase in height the further they travelled down the shoreline. Buffeted now by the increased wind they no longer cut through the deep swells but would go up one side, crest out and then plummet into a trough. Water began to spill into the boat and Chico bailed as quickly as he could from the centre seat. He could hear the motor roaring as the back end came out of the water on the downside of each wave. At times the men felt as if they were floating on nothing as they peaked out on the crests. He couldn't believe how quickly the wind had gone from a ripple to these huge waves.

Their trip down had been rough but not life threatening. Now he wondered if they would make it back to Old Woman beach. They couldn't go ashore as the incoming waves would crush the boat against the steep cliffs. They could easily flip if they hit a submerged rock and the only hope was to keep going and hope they didn't swamp or turn over in the massive swells.

Wave after wave came charging at them as Rick gamely hung onto the throttle arm desperately hoping the boat wouldn't flip or sink with all the incoming water. Chico could not keep up with the amount being washed in. At times he had to hang on for dear life to keep from being washed overboard. This was by far the most scary adventure they had ever had. Any concerns he might have had of the things they had seen and heard on Chaillon Lake were long forgotten and replaced by the very real possibilities of being sent into the cold waters of Superior. To the amazement of both men they remained calm through the terrifying experience.

After what seemed an interminable time they could see Old Woman beach, but they were still a long way from shore. They would need to make a fast run in and hope the back end of the boat did not fill up with water.

After a few tense moments the bow of the boat ground to a halt in the sand a few feet short of dry land. Chico jumped over the side into two feet of water and hauled with all his strength as Rick shut the motor off and lifted it out of the water.

Chico then strode up onto the sand beach, bent over and kissed the ground. Never was he so happy to be on solid terra firma. The calmness he had felt while going through the ordeal was replaced by a strange weakness that overcame him for a few seconds.

"I'm real glad that's over, chum," Rick said as he pulled their packs from the boat.

"That's for sure," came the reply. "Give me a hand to get that canoe out of the boat."

Fifteen minutes later they had loaded all the gear in the back of the truck and were busy lashing down the boat and canoe to the racks on the truck when Chico looked out over the bay.

"Look at that, Rick, the wind has gone down and the lake is calm again. What's that all about?"

"Strange for sure. But remember how calm the water became after we arrived on Bushy Bay on the way in?"

"Yeah, and what about the guy with the white hair

yelling at us from the beach after we left? Maybe he was trying to warn us."

"That's right, but we'll never know, will we. One thing for sure, I did a lot of praying on this trip, and God was faithful and brought us back safely. Let's give the Lord our thanks for answered prayer.

5. PERILOUS JOURNEY

PROLOGUE:

The 38 road begins at Highway 17 north of Sault Ste. Marie, Ontario and follows the Chippewa River for several miles, then continues to mile 80 on the Algoma Central Railroad. In the summer the ride in by truck can be a long and often a slow drive of some thirty plus miles, but very picturesque. In the winter one must use a snowmobile as the road is not plowed. The ride can be bumpy and energy consuming in the best of weather and very tiring if the weather conditions are not good. The following story of peril and mishap is about a man and wife who lived on Spruce Lake a few miles from the 38 road and often used the road to bring in supplies both in winter and summer.

Ted was a trapper of fur bearing animals who worked full time at the local steel mill as a millwright. A stocky man with a solid body and of somewhat less than average height, he was a true outdoorsman. Often with his full black beard and black hair he resembled many of the mountain men of old. His wife once said Ted could be happy living in a shack with cracks in the wall big enough to throw a cat through. Once retired, his wife Jean and he planned to sell their home in the small hamlet of Searchmont and move to their cabin on Spruce Lake, mile 71 on the ACR.

Jean was a woman who although of small stature had vitality and willpower, the qualities she would need in order to live in the wilds of northern Ontario. Mixed with compassion and kindness she was a good partner for her husband the trapper.

They had built a log cabin during the '80s and had spent a great deal of time on the lake, both in winter and summer. During the early '90s the couple planned to put a two story addition on the back of their existing camp. Ted began to cut and haul logs to the property with the help of several friends, using snowmobiles during the winter of '93. In the spring as the days grew warmer he and Jean began the arduous task of peeling the logs.

Peeling the bark off spruce logs on warm spring days when the blackflies have hatched is an experience most do not wish to have, unless it is absolutely necessary. Once the logs are cut the best time to peel is when the logs are still green and full of sap, and the warmer weather facilitates the process. Thus here we have our intrepid pair of bush folks slaving away in the heat using two homemade draw knives made from metal leaf springs.

Ted seemed to revel in the task but his wife struggled at times with the droves of the little black insects that incessantly flew in her eyes, ears and mouth. The same routine carried on daily: take a breath, swallow a bug, cough, take a drink. Even with bug juice slathered on, the little pests still kept coming and Jean would often resort to putting on a head net, causing her to perspire even more.

Once the logs were skinned of their bark, they were left to dry through the summer. During these months Ted built a front deck on the cabin and began the strenuous job of pouring the cement pads for the new addition.

Ted's brother Rod came often to help out with the hard work and was extremely appreciated beyond what words Ted could express. The summer days were hot but he worked on, being totally exhausted at the end of each day.

During the years of 1993 and '94, Ted used his vacation time and weekends to work unendingly to the close of each day.

The couple would often head to town during this time on the 38 road to pick up friends or supplies and stay for a day and head back the following morning.

In the summer months, they would leave their truck parked at the bottom of the Quintette Lakes and take their boat down the chain of lakes, as did many others who stayed on Spruce Lake or the Quintettes.

The boaters used a type of ladder with a winch to raise and lower their craft between lakes One and Two. The Quintette Lakes were comprised of three lakes that had to be traversed by boat for those going to Spruce Lake with a portage between McGully Lake (aka Lake Three) and Spruce as the final leg. Ted and Jean would use an ATV to take supplies on the last leg of their journey. This was a much shorter trip than driving the road to the east end of Spruce and then having to transport supplies by boat to the west end where their cabin was situated. They left a larger boat on the bottom of the Quintettes (Lake One) and a smaller one on McGully, which worked best except for the times when the wind was up, which made the trip in the smaller boat somewhat hazardous.

During the fall of '96 Ted retired from Algoma Steel and moved to the cabin full time in mid October. The snow began to fall early that year, and Jean was unable to stay till mid November due to other commitments that kept her in town. The weather by now was nasty and cold, making travel on the lakes very miserable and dangerous. Many times they had to break the ice that was forming along the edges in order to cross the lakes.

Hardships may come in various ways when people have a vision or a dream that drives them on. The man Ted and his wife Jean had this dream and were now prepared to see it to fruition. Our story to follow is one that caused great adversity and trouble, but is one that could happen to anyone who challenges the elements of winter in the north.

HARDSHIP ON THE 38TH ROAD:

April had arrived. The winter had begun to shed its heavy coat of white snow, especially in the open areas where the sun was able to penetrate. Spring was in the air and all living life was excited and stirring around. There was still lots of ice on the lakes in the north but the edges were beginning to deteriorate making the time short for the snowmobiles. Some were still seen skimming across the packed surfaces en route to different lakes for the last chance to go ice fishing. Many however looked forward to the warmth of the spring and boating and using their all-terrain vehicles.

On a particular spring-like day, Ted had travelled to Sault Ste. Marie, the closest big town, and ordered a new Honda Foreman ATV. Purchasing supplies, he brought some back to camp in his sleigh and left the remainder at his brother's house till he came to pick up his new machine. The major storms of the winter had passed and now would come the rains and melting and he hoped to bring in his new 4X4 ATV before the break-up. He planned to head back to town in a few days to pick up the machine and bring it in over the packed trails while they were still hard enough to travel on.

Kirk, a strong young man, had come back with Ted on the snowmobile to help cut the next winter's wood. As the day's passed the pair worked hard, cutting and hauling firewood over the softening snow. Many nights they finished late. Usually weary and worn out they would stumble into the hot cabin and collapse at the wooden kitchen table, ravenous for the steamy dishes of food Jean would place before them.

Excitement mounted in Ted's heart as he waited for the day he would go to town and pick up his new machine. Although the days had been warm he felt he could still come back over the packed trail on the 38 road.

Finally the long awaited day arrived, and Ted and Kirk prepared to take the large snowmobile and head to town to pick up the ATV. Jean would stay at camp and keep the fire burning. She felt reasonably safe as she kept a set of cross country skis and a pair of snowshoes at the cabin in the event she needed to go up the lake for help.

Unfortunately one big problem had arisen. The weatherman was forecasting a rare winter storm with heavy snow due to arrive on that very weekend.

"Ted, I think it would be a lot safer to wait out this big storm that's coming," Jean said as she looked worriedly at her husband.

The men had gone outdoors and were ready to leave. He looked up at the early Sunday morning sky that had begun to fill with large ominous dark clouds. Indeed he thought, there was a storm approaching but they should have time to get to town before the snows came.

"We'll be ok, the storm should pass by tomorrow and we'll come back with both machines. We have to get them in before the break-up or we'll never be able to," Ted responded.

Jean was deeply worried and had a strange premonition that something bad was about to happen. It was a deep seated feeling that was dark and scary but she knew better than try to change her husband's mind. He could be stubborn as a mule at times and she knew this was one of those times.

Ted and Kirk left on the big snowmobile with Kirk on the back. The two headed out on the trail across the Quintettes as tiny snowflakes began to fall.

Ted knew in his heart it would be better to wait but he was a driven man and as they motored along he felt good just to be in the fresh air. It was better to be outside being active than sitting around a hot cabin waiting. Still it was unusual for him to disregard the dire weather forecast as he knew the wilderness could be unforgiving and trouble could arise at any time.

As they headed off the final lake and sped towards the main road he slowed the machine to a stop.

"Kirk, look behind you. Did we bring any snowshoes?"

"Nope," came the reply.

"How could I have forgotten to put them in?" the older man mumbled to himself. That was unlike him to forget something as important as snowshoes.

An hour later they arrived at the corner of Highway 17N and the 38 road. They parked the snowmobile next to Ted's truck that had been left in the Holmberg yard close to the main road. As they climbed into the half-ton, the snow was beginning to come down. The highway would be slippery but it would not take long to make the trip to town if they were careful. He had a trapper's workshop to attend in a couple of hours and then planned to stay over the Sunday and visit with his brother and sister-in-law.

Monday morning found Ted up early, waiting with his trailer at the Honda dealer to load his new Foreman ATV. He had packed the rest of the groceries for camp in the back of his truck, and as soon as the machine was loaded he headed over to Kirk's home to pick him up. The weatherman had been right. The snow mixed with rain had kept coming down all the previous day and was still coming. Visibility was poor and the driving was treacherous even for a 4X4 truck.

Ted drove slowly and watched his trailer behind with the ATV tied tightly down to the sides. Once back at the Holmberg's they parked the truck and unloaded the machines and groceries. Kirk would drive the snowmachine and the sleigh loaded with the supplies and Ted would ride his 400 Honda on the hard packed snow trail all the way to camp.

The trip in began well with Kirk driving the 500 Polaris snowmobile and Ted out front on his new ATV. The main trail seemed hard enough at first but the day had begun to warm and the snow kept coming down, wet and heavy. Although the snowmobile was working well and staying on the main track, such could not be said for the ATV. A short way in Ted's machine began to slide off the sides and sink deep in the soft snow.

Churning and spinning, he was constantly hitting the gas throttle as he tried to stay on the main part of the packed trail.

Frustration was mounting as he kept slipping and sinking. The warm weather was wreaking havoc with the old snowmobile tracks. Several times he had to get off the ATV in order to lift it back on. Kirk would often stop and walk ahead to help his friend. Mile after mile went by as Ted worked the gas and steering trying to keep going despite the terrible conditions.

As they rounded a corner a single snowmobile came towards them. The pair recognized Eli, a man who owned a camp on a small lake about five miles north of Spruce, well known for excellent moose hunting. There were rumours that he had killed at least five bear over the last few years. As the stories went the bears had kept coming back to his camp as if there was a beaten path to his door. One time they had torn a sheet of plywood from his wall and entered and the next time the bear came he was fed a dose of double-0 buck and a slug. All this was rumour, and no one was thinking of bears as Eli stopped his machine.

"Hello. Are you planning to go all the way to camp today?" Eli asked with a look of incredulity on his face.

"Yes, we should make it," came the reply.

"I wouldn't try it. I just spent an hour digging out of the slush."

"Where was that?"

"A few miles past where your trap shack is. It's a wide flooded area and very deep. I was bogged down a long time," Eli responded.

Ted looked over at Kirk and then turned the key on the ATV. His eyes had taken on a steely vacant look. Kirk knew the signs, he'd seen that look before in Ted. The stubborn resolve to move on. Hell or high water, he would keep going.

"You'd better stop and stay at your trailer, Ted," were the last words Eli got out before Ted pulled on his helmet and drove off, the big wheels spinning wildly in the soft snow.

In a short while Ted realized he was expending far too much energy.

He began to have an asthma attack as his strength waned. He pulled out a puffer and drew the vapour deep into his lungs. He was having a difficult time breathing and was sweating profusely and having intermittent coughing spells.

"Kirk, I think we've only come ten miles or so. I'd better leave the four-wheeler on the side and come back for it tomorrow," Ted rasped sourly. He hated the idea of leaving a brand new ATV on the side of the road, but he knew they wouldn't make it to camp before dark at the slow speed they were going.

"Good idea, Ted, this wet snow is making the trail even softer and you're looking really tired," Kirk responded.

Indeed the hard work of steering in the heavy snow and the pushing and shoving for the past ten miles had exhausted the heavy man to a point where he appeared ready to collapse.

"I think I can handle the snowmobile alright, Kirk, if you get on behind me. We have enough time to make it to camp before dark. The Polaris is working well and the long track will keep us up on top of the trail."

The boughs of the trees along the road hung down from the accumulated weight of the snow. Although the sight was beautiful and well suited for a winter postcard scene the two men took no notice. The white stuff kept coming down making visibility extremely difficult and travelling very slow. No one else came down the road; they had seen no one since leaving the main highway. The storm had compelled even the hardiest to burrow in and be patient.

In a short time Ted felt a tap on his shoulder from behind. Slowing down he looked sideways as Kirk was pointing at something. He couldn't make out what he was saying through his helmet and the roar of the Polaris but he knew what Kirk was trying to convey. They were passing the big gravel pit on the left where Ted kept his small trapping trailer. That meant they had come 26 kilometres and still had a long way to go. The thought crossed his mind that maybe they should pull in and stay overnight and wait out the storm. No, they had time to make it to camp, which would be warmer and give them time to have a good rest before heading back to get his other machine. He kept the throttle depressed.

The miles slipped by as the two men slowly made their way through some wet areas and deeper gullies of snow. With the decreased visibility, they would often slide sideways and have to readjust the machine with a lift. And then it happened. As the large snowmobile with the two big men and the sleigh full of supplies began to cross a wide area in the road covered with ice and snow, disaster struck. Ted gunned the snowmobile as they broke through the first layer of ice but they only sunk deeper in the water filled gulley. The tracks of the big Polaris sprayed water for a dozen feet behind. They slowly moved across the wide expanse but the back end sunk deeper and deeper in the slush.

Finally they reached the far embankment and could move no further. They were sitting on a precarious angle with the front end tilted to the sky. Water covered the rear of the machine and Kirk was sitting in it. With the engine still running, Ted yelled for Kirk to get off and start shoving.

Kirk climbed off and immediately sank through the icy water, nearly to his hips. His snowsuit suddenly became heavy with the water. He began to push with all his might trying to get the machine over the steep incline but to no avail. Ted jumped off and the two of them shoved with all the strength they could muster but the machine sunk even further into the icy pool of slush. Ted was now soaked to the waist from the cold frigid water and began to have another asthma attack, coughing violently. Taking several puffs on his inhaler he tried to relax.

He knew they were in serious trouble with the snow still coming down and both of them saturated from the frigid water.

Pulling out a jack from his sleigh, Ted slid the lever under the back bumper of the snowmobile but the bottom of the jack kept sinking deep in the mire below. Time and again they tried to lift the machine but all attempts failed.

"What do you think we should do, Ted?" Kirk studied Ted's face.

"We're in a pickle for sure," came the response.

"How far to camp?" Kirk asked.

"Too far, way too far; we'll do better to try to make it back to the trailer."

"How far is that? Kirk asked dubiously.

107

"I'd say close to 7 miles."

Kirk looked at Ted for a long moment.

"Do you think you can make it through this snow and slush?"

Ted did not respond but walked back to the sleigh and pulled up a corner of the tarp and began scrounging around. Finally he came back with a jar of peanut butter, a loaf of bread and a dozen eggs. Taking his packsack off the back of his snowmachine he stuffed the food inside and slung the pack on his back.

"Come on, we've a long way to go and there's no use wasting time."

Two days had passed since Ted and Kirk had left Jean at the cabin. Two long days for Jean, alone and no way to tell how things had gone for the travellers. Usually she could have used the Quatra, a radio phone to talk to relatives or friends in the Sault, but for some reason the storm seemed to have caused it to be out of order. The main storm had struck late Saturday night, first with snow and then rain, sleet, thunder and lightning. Even her dogs Bud and Brandy had crawled under the table shaking from the noise of the wind and thunder. On the Sunday with the phone still not working she had gone about some of the chores inside but whenever she looked out the window the skies remained dark and foreboding.

The snow kept coming, never ending it seemed to the lady holed up inside the darkened building, all alone with a mixture of trepidation and worry. The warmer weather had brought rain at first but now the temperature had fallen and the heavy white stuff was coming down heavier and heavier. She wondered how the men would ever get back through this much snow, especially with an ATV.

Picking up some crocheting, she worked away with her hands hoping to keep her mind off all the possibilities. Occasionally she looked out on the lake hoping to see some activity but all was still. On the past Friday her neighbours had heard the forecast and hightailed it for town. Smart she thought, and here she was all alone on the lake, not knowing where her husband was. She had made several trips outside to the wood binney on the porch and had shovelled a new path to the wood shed. Perhaps five times already she had snowshoed down to the lake to clear the water hole of the forming ice and brought back several pails of water to place on the stove.

Monday came and the storm was still strong. Around the noon hour she headed over to Mac's old camp where there was another phone. Mac, the former owner, had passed on, but they had access to the cabin. After several tries she was able to get through to a sister in town who unfortunately had no idea where Ted was.

The phone was cutting out periodically so Jean decided to walk home. A few hours later as dusk approached, she began to get seriously worried, wondering if the two men had attempted the trip in. She sure hoped not, but if they had they should have arrived by now.

Through another night of worry Jean slept fitfully and rose early. Now it was Tuesday and perhaps the guys had been wise enough to stay in town one more night and would come out today. She sat in her rocker knitting and began to reminisce of times past. As the day wore on, her stress level rose, and with night coming on she knew they weren't coming this day either. With the darkness came the feeling of dread and fear. Her emotions began to overcome her as tears welled up inside. She knew she must keep active and make plans for the following day. She began to pray with urgency and a cry for help to her God. To this point her faith in Jesus her Lord had brought her through many trials, but tonight she was being tested in an area like never before. Many times waiting is far more difficult than being actively involved in a bad situation, and sometimes there is little anyone can do other than pray and be patient. Those are the times when an active faith and one that believes God is in control is all there is to sustain one's hope. She began making plans to either try snowshoeing out or try phoning Sault Search and Rescue the next day. The only other thought was someone would come down the lake that she might ask to go look for her lost husband.

The Wednesday morning came in bright. The storm with all its fury had passed, and the sun was shining off the new snow making a wonderful winter wonderland. To Jean the day brought hope. She snowshoed back over to Mac's camp and began to phone. Finally she reached the Sault Search and Rescue office and asked if they would check out the 38 road for any signs of humans. Although hopeful as she began making her way back to her cabin, she could not stop thinking the worst. The day was bright but her heart was heavy.

"Ted, you ok?" Kirk asked the older man who had slowed to a crawl.

The only response was a deep guttural hacking cough. Ted's face turned red as he tried to breathe. One more time he reached for the inhaler he carried in his pocket.

Kirk felt they had made good progress considering the heavy snow on the trail and Ted's asthmatic condition. They had walked at least two miles in the moist snow, sinking with every step that forced them to lift each foot and push forward.

Ted had two more coughing jags along the way, but this one was far worse.

With the extra exertion and loss of oxygen, his lungs were screaming for air.

Sweating profusely the men stood alone, far from civilization and any hope of help. They knew they must keep going as they would slowly succumb to hypothermia once they began to cool down. Coupled with the wet clothes and the loss of body fluids, expending this much energy slogging through the soft snow would in time weaken them.

"Let's keep going, Kirk," rasped Ted as he rose from his knees. He couldn't remember when he had felt this tired. He had to move on.

Kirk watched him and hoped they could do another two miles but began to wonder if his friend could make it.

The going was getting tougher as the day wore on. Kirk was feeling a little tired but he was a young man still with a great deal of stamina. His partner had slowed down and seemed to be barely moving at times. How many times had they stopped for rest? He had lost all track of the number or even the time of day. He hoped they were getting close to the old gravel pit but he couldn't tell.

It was afternoon and the cooler air was moving in.

Ted was beginning to feel the chill. No longer sweating as he had, he could feel his body temperature dropping. Inwardly he began to wonder if he had the strength to keep going. They shouldn't be far now, perhaps only a mile or so he hoped.

"Ted, are you ok?" Kirk's voice brought him out of his trance.

"My legs feel like stumps and my chest feels like it might bust, but we'll give it another try."

Another mile found the two men at the gravel pit where the trailer sat. Stepping off the main trail, Kirk sunk to his hips in the soft snow. They had been sinking steadily even on the main trail, which had made the going slow. Several times Ted could barely get his foot up and moving forward, but now they had no trail to walk on and with every step they sunk deep in the heavy snow.

Seeing the end of their ordeal gave the pair an extra lift. Within a few feet both men were crawling forward trying to move through the wet snow in their soggy snow-suits. Many times on their hands and knees they lurched ahead, often crawling along, trying not to sink deep in the snow. Over a half hour later, totally exhausted, Kirk and Ted finally made it to the old trailer.

The man had called it his trap shack, and it sat in the far end of the gravel pit out of sight of the road. Desolate and cold looking, Kirk wondered how they would ever get warm again. He was happy his friend had made it but they could still succumb to the cold if they couldn't get the inside of the trailer warm. He wondered how his friend could heat the place, at least enough for them to warm up, but knew the trapper had stayed in the winter here before.

Although the snow had abated and the day had warmed up to above freezing Ted was chilled to the bone from the loss of body fluids and the exhausting walk in wet clothes. Having used all the bottled water, they were unable to replace the fluids. He felt he had reached the end of his rope.

His fingers shook as he fumbled with the key to unlock the trailer.

Stepping inside, the cold, damp interior air swept over him. This felt colder than outside. Kirk waited on the step and tried clearing some snow away, waiting for Ted to get the propane stove going. The trailer was small and did not have enough room for the two big men to move around comfortably.

"Kirk, get in here and get those wet clothes off. I have two sleeping bags. We'll get in them and warm up once I get this other small stove started."

Kirk entered the musty cold room and tried to focus. The inside was dark and dreary. He felt he'd rather stay out but knew he needed to rest and eat.

Ted handed him a small bucket and asked him to get some snow and bring it in. He soon placed the snow in a large saucepan on a burner and cracked a jug of frozen water into the pan. Hopefully they would have some water in a short time.

The men hung their wet clothes from the ceiling and climbed into the sleeping bags to warm up. Kirk thought Ted was mumbling as he couldn't understand much he was saying. He closed his eyes trying to listen. The room went still. Outside some small critters heard the sound of grunting and snorting.

A human visitor would have recognized the sound of snoring.

Several hours later Ted awoke with a start. Night had arrived and all was dark. He swung out of bed. His throat was dry and parched. He needed to drink water. He looked at the burners on the stove that were still on. The one with the frozen water and snow had been on low and held only a trace of water.

Kirk opened his eyes to see Ted pulling on an old set of dry pants. He wondered what he would wear. His friend pulled on his snow boots and went out to get more snow for melting. Once back in he pulled out the loaf of bread and jar of peanut butter and the dozen eggs from his packsack. Looking through the cupboards he found a box of crackers and a frozen can of soup. Not much for sure, but should keep them going for a day or so.

Ted took six eggs from the pack of a dozen and began to fry them on the stove. He found a hand held grill and placed two pieces of bread on it to toast over a spare burner. Kirk was ravenous and the smell of cooking increased his hunger. Always a big eater, he barely could wait as his stomach screamed for food. Ted had found some old instant coffee and poured it into a small pot of boiling water, and even that smelled good to the young man.

After the small meal they settled in for the night. The inside of the trailer was warm but far from cozy. The night brought colder air keeping the trailer cool so they crawled back in their bags and discussed at length what they should do the next day.

The two men slept well into the morning. The trip the day before had taken a toll on their bodies and they needed the rest. Kirk felt tired but Ted felt sore and worn out. The worst of the storm had passed but a wind was blowing and light snow was in the air. Kirk, who liked cooking, made breakfast from the remaining eggs. They decided to spend the day resting and waiting, hoping someone on the way in would stop and give them a lift to their stuck machine.

However as the afternoon passed they knew they must do something.

They had hoped Jean had been able to reach Ted's brother Rod by phone but realized she must not have and no one was coming. Their bodies would need food and drink to keep going.

The next morning Ted was up early. Taking a large piece of cardboard he found a marker and wrote on it in big letters the word "HELP" and a big arrow pointing towards the back of the gravel pit and the trailer. Finding a long wooden stake from outside he nailed on the sign.

"Kirk, would you take this sign out to the road and stick it in the snow bank?" Ted asked the young man. No one had come so they decided to put up a sign asking for help. The sun was shining brightly as he struggled through the deep snow, but now he felt refreshed and it felt better to be out in the fresh air once more. He hoped someone would see the sign and come in.

Early afternoon arrived and no one had come down the road. Their spirits, once hopeful, began to sag as the sun moved across the sky. Ted was becoming increasingly worried, and his mind was trying to decide what they should do if no one came in. They would run out of propane soon and then things would get really miserable. He went outside and planned to start an outdoor fire when he heard the sound of snowmobiles coming from the west. His heart skipped a beat and hope was renewed. He waited for several minutes listening to the roar of the engines as they came closer, and he yelled to Kirk inside. The younger man came out to stand with Ted waiting for the help they hoped was coming.

As they listened, one machine seemed to have gone by and then the next. Dumbfounded they stood like statues in the snow. All hope was dashed. How could the travellers have missed the sign they put out? Why would they roar by without coming in? Many thoughts crossed their minds as they turned to go inside, their faces crestfallen.

At the log cabin on Spruce Lake, Jean was returning from Mac's camp when she heard snowmobiles coming from the direction of the Quintettes. She had finally made contact with the Sault Search and Rescue, and they had promised to mobilize and go on a search for her husband and Kirk. Relieved that she could at least talk to someone she hurried to get back to camp.

A few minutes later three machines came roaring into the front yard of the camp. There she talked to the men who told her they had found Ted's snowmachine bogged down in deep water at a huge pool on the road on their way in. Two of them had worked away to free his big machine and clear the track that was full of frozen slush and get it going while Steve went back to get Ted.

Relief washed over Jean as she listened. Her prayers had been answered as she thanked the men for all their help. To her they were helping angels. She thanked God the men had come.

As they left she hurried back to Mac's camp to phone and tell Sault Search and Rescue that the men had been found.

A short time later the sound of a single engine could be heard through the trailer's walls. Ted and Kirk rose quickly and headed outdoors and watched a snowmobile plow through the deep snow coming right to where they stood.

"Hi guys. We found your Polaris frozen in the pool of water down the road. You must have had a time getting back here in the storm?" Steve said with a quizzical look on his face.

"That's an understatement," Ted responded. "Did you see my ATV?"

"We sure did. I can't believe you tried to bring it in here in the storm."

"I won't try that again, that's for sure. I thought I'd die on Monday trying to walk back here."

"Jump on behind and I'll take you back to your snow-mobile. The guys should have your machine out of the water by now. I'll come back for your friend."

A desperate situation ended well as Ted and Kirk followed their friends a short time later on the Polaris. After a two day rest at the cabin, the men ventured back out on the 38 road to retrieve the stranded Honda four-wheeler. The temperature had dropped, making the trail stiffer, and after a hard day on the trail they were able to finally get the machine to camp. Thus ends our story that could easily have ended in tragedy. Many things could have happened and this story would not have ended so well and is a tribute to the two men who endured the ordeal.

6. TREACHEROUS ICE

Travelling by snowmobile in late April on the Quintette Lakes was often a treacherous proposition. Mind you, travelling on any of the lakes north of Sault Ste. Marie in mid to late April could be a dicey proposition, regardless of the experience or time spent in the north.

The man and wife known as Ted and Jean had lived at their cabin on Spruce Lake for the past few years. Some would say they both had experience with the changing conditions through out the year. Ted had for many years been a trapper in the area and had survived his share of mishaps. Jean as well was able to relate several harrowing experiences on the ice and on the trail.

Our story begins to unfold with Ted making a trip into town to purchase food and supplies before the spring break-up. Time was quickly running out to make trips across the lake, and several weeks would pass before they could use their boats.

Jean and Ted left their log cabin early one frosty morning and sped across Spruce Lake, over the portage trail and out onto McGully Lake. The day was going to be sunny and warm, which meant the ice would melt faster. Jean would take the Polaris back to camp while Ted drove his truck down the 38 road to town. He would stay with his brother and his wife for a few days, picking up enough supplies such as extra propane, dog food, gas and groceries to see them through the spring break-up.

Quickly they flew over the ice on the packed trail and were soon across all three lakes that led to the parking area where he had left the truck parked.

As he sped off the lake with Jean on the back they felt the back end of the snowmobile sink in the slush at the point where the trail came up on land.

He gunned the machine and made it to safety but realized it had been a close call. He knew they would need to be very cautious from now on when travelling on the ice. The lakes were thawing, especially along the shoreline where the sun shone and the ice had turned to slush and become weak.

"Be careful, Jean, getting back on the ice. Keep your speed up as you come down from the ladder," Ted shouted to his wife as he stood on the running board of the truck.

He watched as she sped away on the snow packed surface towards Quintette Lake One.

Taking the windy, rough path past the ladder used for winching up boats, she moved out onto the lake. Although nervous of the conditions, especially the slush that covered a good portion of the lake, she moved rapidly over the surface. Black, dark spots began to appear on top, which she tried to avoid as they signalled weak spots where getting bogged down was a real possibility. Should that happen she would need to leave the machine and trek back to camp using her snowshoes and maybe not have the endurance to make it. Perhaps a snowmobiler going down the lake would give her a ride, if one happened along, but not likely through the week. She hardly ever saw anyone cruising the lakes except on the weekends.

Sometime later Ted drove his truck down the frozen 38 road, which was plowed daily in order to keep the big logging trucks hauling out the logs through the winter. This year they had kept the road open to what they called the Quintette hill, where he and others would leave their vehicles and go on snowmachines.

As he passed McGovern Lake turn-off he thought of his trapper shack nestled a few hundred yards back in the bush. Well, truthfully it was a small trailer he called a shack. His mind began to recall some of the trips from the past he had gone on in order to check his trapline.

He remembered one time specifically, likely because of the present ice conditions on the lakes.

The time had been in late November and he was busy checking out his traps almost every day. He would leave his trailer in the morning and make his way on the snowmobile to several ponds and waterways where he had set traps. Once he was close enough he would either go on snowshoe or on foot down to the hole on the ice and pull up the trap to see if an animal had taken the bait.

On this one morning he was able to follow his old path down to the edge of the pond and then make his way to the hole without the use of snowshoes. As he came within four feet of the stake holding the chain running under the water, he suddenly felt the ice break under him and he plunged down into the frigid water below.

Ted was a short stocky man who weighed well over two hundred pounds. As the ice gave way, he had no time to jump or move but sunk rapidly into the freezing water. His heart pounded as the adrenalin rushed through his body while his mind tried to adjust to what was happening. At first he flailed his arms trying to regain his balance but he quickly found himself sinking in the soft bottom he had landed on.

Initially the water had gone over his head but he was able to keep his face above water if he stayed upright.

Turning, he frantically tried to move towards shore but his feet had begun to sink in the miry muck beneath. Although he was not a tall man, Ted was strong and now he needed every ounce of strength to move through the water.

With each step his feet would sink down in the deep muck. Exhausted and cold he finally managed to pull himself up on shore and get his breathing back to normal which helped slow his heartbeat.

For now his mind was racing. Should he start a fire and warm up or try to make it back to the trailer and find some dry clothes and unthaw there? That was a decision he had to make quickly or succumb to the elements and hypothermia.

One of the factors in his decision making was how long would it take him to travel back to his trapper shack. He would need to travel over three miles on the narrow snowmobile path with his clothes frozen stiff and his body temperature dropping. He counted the odds of making it in time. Wisdom dictated he start a fire quickly and get it roaring hot in order to dry out his clothes and warm up.

By now he had walked up the hill to his machine and started the engine. The exhaust warmed his hands and he took time to turn and face the return trail. Already he could feel how much colder he felt as his inner wet clothing was lowering his body temperature.

Ted was not an indecisive man and he made his choice. He started down the trail, moving as quickly as possible along the rough trail. The snow was partially frozen and as he moved along he hoped his extra body weight would keep his vitals warm. He reasoned if he was a thin man he may have started a fire instead.

Ted recalled how he felt when he had arrived back at his trap shack. After warming up the interior and changing clothes he got into his good down sleeping bag.

Even now after all this time, thinking back to that day, he was thankful he made it out and didn't come down with pneumonia after the cold exposure to the elements.

His mind quickly reverted back to the present as he focused on the snow covered road ahead, glad to be in a warm truck and looking forward to a large cup of Tim Horton's double, double coffee.

Jean was sitting at the kitchen table early one morning a few days later when the call came. Ted asked her to bring the small 300 Polaris and sleigh and meet him at the big hill by Lake One at noon today.

Going outside she found to her horror both snowmobiles coated with a thick film of ice. Taking a small hammer, she began to tap at the ice but quickly realized this would take a long time. Every part of the machine was covered. Going back inside she put on warmer clothes and took a glimpse at the time. Ted would be well over an hour before he was at the landing. She was sure she would have the ice off in time, as long as the rain and ice hadn't affected the working parts of the engine of her machine.

After chipping away at the ice for some time, Jean decided to give the starter cord a pull, hoping the snowmobile would start. Often it would be difficult to turn over, especially after a wet night or sudden change in temperature. After a number of yanks her arm was hurting and her stress level was rising as the machine didn't want to start. She knew Ted would be well on his way by now. Resuming her pulling on the cord she exerted all her strength and said a silent prayer. The sound of the motor kicking over came to her ears. One more pull and she throttled the gas to keep it going. Grateful she jumped on the seat and was away.

In a short while she crossed the portage to McGully Lake, being careful to circumvent the trees nearest the trail.

Overnight the ice storm had left a hard crust on the snow giving her grief as she skimmed over the slippery, hazardous parts. Often sliding sideways the steering was extremely difficult and she hoped the trip down the lakes would be easier.

Once out on the open lake she found it a struggle to stay up on the hard packed tracks and had to be careful not to slide into the deeper ruts in the snow and tip over.

Jean crossed Lake One, and as she approached the end she recalled Ted's warning about being careful coming off the ice. She slowed the machine a few yards from the shoreline and then saw how soft the edge looked. With a surge of speed she began to cross over the last part of the ice where it joined solid ground. With a feeling of terror she felt the rear end of the snowmobile sink through the ice behind her. Giving full throttle, the tracks sent water flying in volumes as she made it up on stable ground. Looking back she realized how close she was to not making it.

A short time later after Ted had parked the truck, they loaded her smaller sleigh with supplies, and the two of them headed back to camp. He carefully used a different spot to come out onto the first lake. Although the day was warming up, the icy tracks on the lake made from many trips over the winter were still firm. Without mishap they arrived back to camp. Ted unloaded the goods while Jean chipped off the ice on Ted's snowmobile.

Without taking time for lunch, he started his bigger machine, hooked on his large steel sleigh and was soon heading back to the landing. Jean followed, relieved they only had one more trip. Today was sunny and more ice would melt, making lakes even more treacherous.

As he roared across the ice on his big Polaris, Ted felt great. The wind on his face and the sun in his eyes made him feel good.

He felt thrilled to be back in the bush and knew this was where he belonged. Sure, adversities and hardships were bound to happen, but it was still better to be here than in the city.

The end of the Quintettes came into view.

The closer he came, he could see several spots where the ice seemed strong and safe enough to run up the embankment to the trail that led to his truck. Slowing his machine down within ten feet of the edge he aimed for one spot ahead but suddenly the skis dug into the slush and then sank quickly out of sight. He stood up and swung his leg over the seat as he and the snowmobile continued to sink deeper in the slush. In seconds he was standing in over three feet of water with the entire machine submerged beside him.

Jean sat far back from the edge of the lake on her own sled and watched in helplessness as her husband and the

Polaris went into the water. More stress as she realized they were in a fine pickle and she had no idea what she could do, except watch. Perhaps the time had come for them to consider moving back to town. These mishaps were tough on both her and Ted in different ways and the age thing was indeed a factor.

Ted had moved up on the hard crusted shoreline and waved for her to walk around to where he stood. When she arrived beside him he told her he had to go back in the water and go under the seat where he had a winch stored. That meant he would also get his arms and hands soaked in the icy water as the seat was a foot under water. He told her to take her machine down to the truck for now while he tried to winch his sled up to solid ground where he would attempt to drain the hoses and dry off the engine. Two hours later, he was ready to try to start his snowmobile. Jean had loaded her small sleigh with gear and left the propane bottle and gas containers for Ted to transport, if, and that was a big if, the machine started. At this point in time there was little she could do except pray, and being a Christian woman that was her strength.

Humanly speaking she doubted very much if that machine would ever start, especially out here. In reality only a few would expect the engine to even crank over.

Call it what you will, depending on your view of faith and prayer but on this day whether it was Jean's prayers or Ted's ability to work in adverse conditions when he was wet and cold, or perhaps a combination of both, somehow that big snowmobile coughed and then started.

Sometimes what at first appears to be a hopeless situation can with perseverance, knowledge and the helping hand of God bring you safely through some desperate moments.

Ted drove his machine with Jean back to the truck and loaded the rest of their supplies on his big sleigh. After warming up inside the truck they once again ventured back down the rough trail. They approached the edge of the lake and stopped to weigh their chances of getting out on stable ice from shore. Ted found some planks and small timbers nearby in the bush along with a portion of a wooden dock used in the summer. Jean and he soon dragged the material close to the entry point. A half an hour later they had finished a bridge that stretched from the snowbank on land across to where the ice was strong enough to hold their machines. With some trepidation Ted swept across the wooden platforms out onto the good ice with his machine and trailer as Jean watched from shore. She was nervous of the risky undertaking and now would be her turn to go across the makeshift bridge.

The main concern was staying on the one sheet of plywood as it would be extremely slippery. Should her machine go sideways she would be dumped into four or five feet of water and that would be a nightmare. She viewed the platform ahead and tried to bolster her courage with another short prayer.

She heard her husband yell at her to get moving so she twisted the gas throttle and slowly edged out on the wood.

Very slowly she moved forward with fear but to her surprise the snowmobile did not slip or spin and in a few seconds she made it across.

Ted had been watching and with a sigh of relief he roared off down the lake. Jean was not far behind and happy they were finally headed home.

Without a doubt, there were many ways this story could

have turned out. If the water had been deeper at the edge of the lake, Ted would have been in the same predicament he had found himself at the beaver pond. Here however, he would not have been able to recover his machine. As it was, only a hearty man could have worked in the freezing water for that long a time. Hooking the cable up under the water and winching it out, and then working away getting the fluids drained was a demanding and difficult task only a few sturdy bushmen of his age could accomplish.

In closing we give a tribute to those in the north who are willing to challenge the great outdoors and endure the hardships that can and often do arise in order to enjoy God's wonderful creation.

A final salute to Trapper Ted, who has moved on to glory and left others here on earth to miss him.

7. A CAMPING NIGHTMARE

PROLOGUE:

Throughout the years there have been thousands of outdoor enthusiasts who for the sake of being part of nature have headed for the wilderness. Untold numbers have endured the rigours of the bush in order to enjoy camping, fishing or hunting and others for bird watching, hiking and photography. The story to follow is one which involves the discovery of a lake and the consequent journey to and from the lake by a man and woman. They were to be challenged in ways most would rather not have to endure.. The author hopes you find the story amusing and fun to read as he and his wife take a trip in the woods.

THE DISCOVERY:

In the beginning it was only a thought. More than a thought, it was a question. I loved to explore the lakes and rivers in the Algoma region, especially the remote ones, and presently stood staring at a cluster of small lakes drawn on a topographical map on the dining room table. I was intrigued. There was no name on them and no roads leading to them. Was it possible? Could there be access to these lakes? Were there any fish in them?

Marking the area and calculating a distance of two miles as the crow flies from the nearest road I reached for the telephone and phoned my good friend Glen, who had a similar affliction. Some of you may know what I'm talking about. The affliction some men have and recently a few women as they searched for the one lake that would be the magical "Golden Pond" they had always hoped to find.

The phone rang several times before Glen picked up the receiver.

"Hello."

"Glen, hope I didn't wake you."

"No, I have yet to hit the sack. What's up?

Knowing my friend had worked all night, I wasted no time in small talk.

"Would you like to hike into a remote lake north of here? The lake looks promising and with no roads into it there's a good chance of some good fishing.'

"What kinda of fish would there be?" Glen asked, realizing full well he was setting himself for some disastrous adventure.

I hedged the answer slightly. "Er, I'm not certain, but I imagine either lake trout or brook trout." I knew my friend enjoyed catching and eating lake trout and pickerel but had no such inclination for brookies.

To my surprise Glen responded sleepily, "Sounds good. Find out as much as you can about the lakes. Let me know when you want to go. Phone me later." The phone went dead.

Later that day I phoned a man associated with the Ministry of Natural Resources in Sault Ste. Marie and gleaned some interesting data of the area. The forestry airplanes had indeed landed on these lakes in the past and should there be any roads accessing the lakes they would be rough and overgrown.

Further good news indicated the lakes had been stocked in the past and fished from the pontoons of their flying machines.

The trail of events leading to the discovery of a lake that would become known as "Beach Lake" had begun. I initially nicknamed the lake "No Name Lake" simply for the lack of a better one before discovering a lovely beach with fine sand. The fact the wind always blew in hurricane force right at us never deterred us from spending several warm weeks on this remote spot.

A few days later Glen agreed to hike with me on a hot day in June with the blackflies at their peak and the bush soaking wet from the rain the night before.

A short drive of two hours on an old logging road found us smashing through the dense bush hoping to find the promised lake.

I brought a map and a compass, which over the past forty years was all I ever used for exploring new areas. Extra work perhaps, especially if your calculations are not quite right but who needed the new fangled gadget called a GPS when searching for your treasured dream. So what if a GPS took you right to the exact spot in half the time, I probably would struggle with how to work the dog-gone thing anyway and leave it at home in the drawer.

After two hours of wandering through the wet bush, eating blackflies and sweating off several pounds of flesh, we stopped for a rest and ate a granola bar, washing it down with a drink of lukewarm liquid.

"We must be close," I assured Glen. He hoped we hadn't gone past the end of the lake. "Don't worry, we're not lost."

Glen gave me a look that was a mixture of mistrust and hatred for bringing him on this wild goose chase. He had worn only a sailor type of pants that left his legs from the knees down fully exposed and now his legs had become covered with scratches, bug bites and blood. He had worn running shoes instead of hiking boots, which had become soaked from the moisture still dripping from the brush. Watching him, I could tell that in his heart he planned to never let himself be talked into going on another hike with me.

Once rested we moved forward on what we hoped would be the final leg of the journey. The two of us had been steadily crashing through the dense bush for some time when we came upon a steep ridge with a small creek at the bottom.

"That must be the stream that flows into the lake we're looking for," I chortled, much relieved. We began to make our way down the side of the hill and in a remarkably short time could see blue water through the trees. Without a word we continued on and finally reached the rocky shore of a lake that appeared to be a good size. Pulling out the map, we spread it out on a large flat rock, studying the area intently, desperately hoping this was the lake we had planned to find. If it wasn't, my already shaky reputation as a bushman would be in serious jeopardy. I would need to sell all the outdoor equipment accumulated over the past forty years and plan to sit on the St. Mary's riverfront watching the boats go by, reminiscing of days long past.

The lake appeared to be close to a half a mile in length and the same in width, with several bays and a few islands. Yes, this must be the unnamed lake we had hoped to find.

Relief combined with a sense of exhilaration washed over our tired bodies after the long hike through the wet brush with the never ending mobs of blood sucking insects continually attacking. We were thankful we had finally found this place of seclusion and tranquility without missing the lake entirely and heading off into the wild unknown.

After a short rest we walked out to a small point of land that gave us a better view of a beautiful remote lake and a promise of great things to come.

I sat on a rock feeling my age. Close to sixty years old I no longer had the energy of a few short years ago. The sun was warm and I appreciated the heat but felt thirsty from the loss of body fluids. Gulping down a large amount of water I watched Glen move down the shoreline jumping from rock to rock. A hint of envy swept through me briefly as my feet no longer could sustain the impact of landing on hard surfaces due to arthritis. Nonetheless I was happy to still be able to hike and enjoy the bush. Life would not be the same if one was unable to enjoy the feel of nature and the challenge of the outdoors.

Glen was shouting something. At first I couldn't make out what he was saying. A few minutes later I heard his voice once more. "John, do you see something shiny way down in the far bay?"

We had not brought binoculars and had to scan the far shoreline with naked eyes. A weird feeling was forming in the pit of my stomach, a sinking feeling of sadness and disappointment.

Here we were, after hiking through swamp, over steep hills, through tight bush, battling a multitude of blood sucking insects to find what appeared to be a human sign.

And then, sure enough, as I strained my eyes I could make out something in a far away bay that definitely had a gleam to it. Perhaps it was only a big white rock, but no, in my heart I knew it was a boat. That only left one conclusion: others were fishing this lake. Another thought came swiftly to mind as well.

Perhaps my friend Glen was devising a plan to get even with the guy who led him to a so called remote lake, to find instead an already well used fishing spot.

With that in mind I slowly made my way through the edge of the woods around the bay, hoping whatever we were seeing was something other than a boat. After a long exhausting hour of weaving through the tag alders and brush along the side of the lake we finally came to a halt. We stood staring at a twelve foot aluminum boat leaning against a tree and even worse could see another boat partially hidden behind some smaller brush. Sadly the realization dawned on us that no one could get boats into this lake without a trail, and if there was a trail then the lake would be ice-fished and summer fished. What a tragic disappointment, a feeling that might even raise the ire of less stable souls. However in the heart of a fisherman there always remains a sliver of hope, that somehow, some way what might look like a lost cause would turn out to be a wish come true.

And so it was that I recalled talking to an old-timer a week before who had heard of the MNR flying into an unknown lake in the area to survey it, and now hoped the boats belonged to them.

That wonderful thought was quickly dispelled when after a short five minute search of the area we found an old snowmobile trail that had not been used for a long time.

Someone in years past had cut a trail to enable others to winter fish the lake. With a perverted sense of humour I found this somewhat humorous after all the work to get here. Never the less I was never quite sure how my friend had dealt with that casual walk in and the loss of a dream. I kept a watchful eye for precautionary reasons of course.

The next plan was to follow the trail in hopes it led out to the good logging road where the truck was parked.

We were a disappointed pair of fishermen to say the least as we began the hike back. Thankful to be in the sunshine and heat of the day following a rough trail, we walked along mumbling to ourselves about the unlikelihood of ever finding a remote lake where no one had ever fished. Both of us agreed it seemed a hopeless dream. However without telling the other, deep within our hearts we would never lose the hope that one day we would find that magical, dreamed about lake filled with elusive speckled trout of gigantic portions.

Hours later Glen and I hiked down a well maintained logging road that led to the parked truck. We had found a snowmobile trail that joined up with a new ATV trail, which led to the main road. In time we staggered up to the truck, exhausted, hot and despondent, simply glad to be able to climb up and sit in the cab and rest our worn out bodies. Perhaps the best news; my friend didn't stop talking to me and in fact we went back to fish the lake a week later. Yes, hope remains eternal in the mind of the die hard fisherman.

Later that year I was able to persuade my wife Mary to come for a vacation in August and here the rest of the story begins, which we have called "A Camping Nightmare."

THE JOURNEY:

Six a.m. found Mary and I climbing into our old Suburban, loaded with every imaginable piece of camping gear we could stuff in. We were headed for our favourite "Beach Lake" that we had camped on for the past three years. Inside the Suburban, items ranged from folding chairs, folding tables, and dining tent to sleeping tent, sleeping bags, and air mattresses.

Along with these we had tote bins full of dry goods and ice chests full of food and our prized possession, an outhouse tent built from aluminum poles and a tarp by our friend Cris that would keep us sitting on the potty in relative comfort away from the critters and blackflies. Samplings of the other supplies were such things as a chainsaw, clippers, and axes as well as fishing gear, outboard motor, gas, oars and a multitude of other equipment. We planned to have a relaxing time with all the comforts of home. No worries, no hardships and a lot of relaxing, I imagine many are already using that name "dreamer" liberally at the moment.

That was our plan on this much anticipated day. I have written of past experiences that may have entered the realm of calamities and misadventures and we knew in our hearts this trip might include certain challenges because of our age and arthritic conditions that seem to come with growing older. Little did we know how many challenges there would be.

In a few moments we were tooling down the highway towing a small trailer with our new Yamaha ATV and a old beat up boat on top of the truck. What could ever go wrong? The day was sunny and warm with little wind and the forecast for the next week was the same. We looked forward to sitting on the beach in the bright sunlight and soaking in the rays, going swimming and catching a few trout. What more could we ask for?

Almost three hours later we pulled off the logging road and into a hidden recess where we parked the Suburban out of sight. I pulled out a small cart from behind the ATV, backed out the small four wheeler and hooked them together. The small trailer had wooden sides and could hold a lot of gear, and that was important. After we loaded up with as much as possible, we tied everything down the best we could, including three, five gallon jugs of city water. (Mary used a lot of water, and we didn't trust the lake water as we could see signs of beaver close to the beach.) If you have never had beaver fever, known as Giardia, I hope you never do as you will never forget the experience. Ever! Of course now we have a bag to filter out all these little parasites etc., which always happens years down the road and far too late.

The first trip down the path was slow with the heavily laden trailer swaying from side to side as we made our way through the deep mud holes filled with water from the past week's rain.

One could say this was the beginning of the nightmare for my dear wife. Mary walked beside the cart and kept it stabilized the best she could.

The water stretched from one side of the narrow road to the other making the walking extremely difficult as she pushed through the close knit tag alders that grew along the edge. Naturally I had the easy job of driving the four wheeler, being more experienced in the operation of an ATV. How convenient was that? The cart with narrow twelve inch tires came close to flipping over several times, but fortunately she was able to keep it upright. The tires would often sink deep in the mud making the going tough and sending mud and water spraying far out in the back. Then there were the boulders sticking up causing the cart to bounce precariously from side to side. Ok, I get it. The wise thing was to have bought the big fat ATV tires designed for floating over the rough rocks and soft places but pure stubbornness and a optimistic mind kept me from doing the best thing.

I would rather not mention any of the comments my wife was saying as she struggled through the muck and the wet tag alders, swatting the hordes of blackflies and mosquitoes. I can be reasonably assured I was no longer on the list of her most favourite people in the world. With that being said she was a great trooper and thankfully didn't poison my supper later that night. Through the many, many years she has been a fantastic cook both at home and in the bush.

I will always be eternally grateful to her as without her help and companionship I would never have made many of the trips to the wilderness.

Onward we went down the trail, wobbling along the best we could until we were past the water holes and over a steep incline. Then we turned down a narrow, rougher road that had been recently cleared. The four wheeler came close to tipping a few times as I moved ahead of Mary, my human stabilizer so to speak. The path was often slanted and the ATV was suspended several times with the wheels spinning in the air as I tried to keep the machine from rolling on its side. Going over the rocks on the upgrades and around trees that edged the trail kept me struggling to maintain balance while still making headway.

Some have said we needed a stronger machine to crawl over the rocks and through the mud while pulling such a heavy load. I can only say we purchase what we think will be adequate at the time. In hindsight we often would do things differently, at least if we can afford the luxury of bigger and better.

At this point I was able to drive a little faster than Mary could walk, so away I went on down the trail. As I rounded a sharp corner on a hill I could see water. Thank goodness, at last we had arrived. The day was moving on and we still had a lot to do to get to camp. Once we had unloaded the gear at the landing we would return for the boat, motor and the remaining supplies. Well, that was the plan except at that very moment the trailer flew up in the air and came down hard on the frame. Without my human stabilizer the cart capsized on its side spilling out a number of the contents.

As disheartening as this was, things went from bad to worse. I would need to unload the trailer before I could sit it upright and reload.

I only had time to unload the provisions and gear etc. when Mary arrived and gave me a hand to lift it back on its wheels. One problem, the cart sat on a slant and it wasn't because of the unevenness of the ground. A tire had blown out and was flat.

"What do we do now?" she croaked. She was thirsty and hot from the long walk down the road. "I hope you brought a spare tire because that one has a huge rip in the side wall."

"Actually, now that I think of it, I believe I left it in the garage," I replied with a dumb look on my face.

"What! How could you forget something like a spare tire? So what's your grand plan now? The weather forecast for today is 90 degrees and humid and here we are, still in the bush."

I may not be a rocket scientist but I can tell when the love of my life is exasperated with me.

As I stood there with my mind whirling, I already had devised a plan. Sadly it involved a lot of carrying and slugging to get the binneys of provisions, the fresh water and all the gear down to the landing at the lake. Reminded me of the years we had portaged from lake to lake in Superior Park north of Sault Ste. Marie. I'm sure she was thinking the same thing. Nothing really ever changes. Especially if you go camping with a husband like hers.

When I suggested my plan, I got a look that would wither the leaves on a palm tree.

"You know what. I'm going down to the lake to cool off, you can carry down this stuff yourself," she retorted as she grabbed a duffel bag and a small propane stove and took off leaving me to stare at her back.

I knew she didn't mean it and would help sooner or later. Guess again, oh great man of optimism. We had broken down at least two hundred yards from the lake and although that may not seem very far, by the time I had carried all the plastic binneys and water jugs down to the landing my arms felt like paralyzed extensions of a long armed gorilla.

An hour later and rested, I dragged the cart down to park it near the lake and we began our journey back to get the boat, motor, gas and a ton of other supplies we would carry inside the boat. By now I was feeling exhausted but hoped a little lunch of sandwiches and Gatorade would revive the spirits. Thankfully Mary returned with me to help and rode on the back of the ATV.

As I recall, the trip last year had not been a barrel of laughs either. In fact I believe we promised ourselves to never do this again. The heat, the exhaustion and the long time it took to get to the campsite didn't seem to be worth it. However here we were and every year seemed to bring some wonderful challenges that we found harder and harder to appreciate. We loved the lake and the time spent on the lake but the trips in and out were brutal. And that's when everything went well.

Once revived, we loaded the boat on a cradle that dragged behind the ATV in form of a *travois* used by Natives long ago. Cris, a wonderful friend who will become part of the story later, had helped me construct this carrying device. After loading the boat with the motor, oars, gas, chainsaw and a number of other useful items, we began our return trip down the road of hell. We always tried to keep in mind the fun and humour in times like these. Let me say, I'm not sure we always succeeded.

I will not go into great detail about the number of tip overs on the way back but someone who believes in Murphy's Law would gladly say I told you so. Suffice to say, Mary my dear wife had to walk alongside once again to steady the contraption, which of course put her into a wonderful state of mind.

We parked our overheated Yamaha four wheeler on a small rise a short distance from the lake and proceeded to load the boat. Incidentally, we had to pull the boat by hand down the grade and through a foot of mud to get to the water because the ATV would have become stuck. That doesn't sound so bad except while carrying down the gear Mary stepped into the muck, which filled her boots. I was in deep do-do again. I will refrain from describing her remarks, except that it was becoming evident we might not have a long marriage.

We finally loaded the boat as much as we could and planned to come back for the rest as soon as possible. Once again Murphy's Law came into play. As I set the motor on the transom, I noticed it was leaking gas. No problem, I began to pull the cord. Over and over I pulled until my arm wore out. Fortunately the leaking gas was going into the boat and truthfully it didn't seem like much. Really.

About this time I took a glimpse at Mary. That was a mistake.

That look some of you guys may know so well. A steely withering look that could melt the ice on a glacier. I made no comment and kept pulling. I had borrowed the small motor and planned to buy it, but the owner had told me it had issues, which we hoped had been fixed. Optimism is a great thing most of the time but we all know what it means if we have issues. That's a recipe for trouble. I kept pulling and pulling, and someone must have been praying because it finally turned over and started. I was beyond grateful, as the boat was heaped high with no room left to move and of course one oar buried under the pile and that set of eyeballs staring at me that would cut through the hardest diamond on earth.

Away we went down the lake, with the propeller bouncing off a number of submerged rocks in the narrow channel I had unadvisedly thought we should take. With the boat overloaded and swaying from side we somehow miraculously made it safely to the beach. There it sat in all its glory and we could tell no one had used the firepit, and the encroaching bush was a jungle that would need cutting. We unloaded the boat and I decided to try to find the problem with the leaky motor. Needless to say, I admit to being somewhat less than a small engine mechanic and although two qualified repairmen had tried to fix it, it now became apparent that all that loving attention had not worked.

I decided to lift the little motor off the transom and take it ashore where hopefully I could stem the leaking problem. Unfortunately during the process my foot slipped, and the motor dropped into three feet of water. By now you might find this story hard to believe, but I assure you the events happened this way. Naturally the outboard motor never ran again for the entire trip.

I asked myself if we were having fun yet. The reader might ask why would I ever tell anyone about our trials and can only say I hope you can laugh with us and find the humour in our trip of mishaps.

As I stood looking out over the clear blue waters of the lake known to us as Beach Lake, I had accepted the fact the only way to transport the rest of the provisions and gear from the landing to the beach was for me to pick up the oars and start rowing. Early afternoon had arrived and the wind had risen which meant my little old arms had to work even harder. The breeze had a cooling effect for sure as the day was indeed hot but there was no time for a swim.

I left my hard working spouse to sort out the first load and I was off in less than rocket speed to bring in the next load.

Many things could have gone differently but as hot as the sun was and as draining the effect on the body, we both were thankful we did not have a cold and rainy day. We had come to spend time enjoying the heat and the sun. The second load down the lake proved to be less than an exhilarating experience, moving at a snail's pace for over a half a mile through a rising chop on the water.

The old song "Row, row, row your boat" kept coming to mind as eternity seemed to pass before my eyes. To say the old body was wearing a little thin would be an understatement. I only hoped the boat didn't fill up with water from the waves washing over the sides or that I inadvertently leaned too far and tipped the whole load in the drink.

As I returned on my way back I could tell Mary had already set up the dining tent and secured it and had carried all the supplies up from the water's edge. God bless her, I thought as I was so tired I didn't want to do anything but rest.

"Hey Hon," she hollered down to me, "after you bring up all the stuff from the boat, you need to set up our sleeping tent, and cut some firewood and clear out the brush from behind the dining tent and..." I no longer could hear anything from the roar of the wind in my ears.

Our story could end there except for two things. Mishap and misery can go hand in hand. We did work hard to clean up the area and had fun swimming and sunning ourselves while trying not to think of the return trip up the road of hell, and oh yes, we still had a flat tire. Ten days of bliss and a little fishing that did produce a few nice trout and some good exercise from rowing. Ten days of rowing can really get your body in shape. Trust me. As well, one begins to enjoy the stillness on the water with only the loons swimming close by, encouraging you on as you row, row, row, with arms growing to the size of Popeye's.

I would like to say at this time in our story that no unforeseen catastrophe happened on our stay at the beach this year, which might surprise you to no end considering all you have already read.

However the year before we had what some might call a near tragic event. Two good friends of mine along with their sons came for a couple nights stay to do some fishing. During one of those days, Rick had decided to start up his Coleman stove, which he had kept for years and which had belonged to his father's father but still worked. He had taken the stove inside the dining tent and placed it on a long table, then fired up the gas burners and was standing over the table waiting for water to heat. Rick is a great cook and we all looked forward to whatever he was planning to prepare for supper.

The rest of the gang was sitting outside enjoying the brilliant sun, swathed in the heat of the day when suddenly from within the tent came a massive explosion. Stunned from the noise we rushed to the opening of the tent and looked in. Fear had gripped our hearts of what might have happened to our chum. To our great relief he now stood in the centre of the tent, still in shock, with no eyebrows and his hair burnt black.

The good news was, although his face was a deep red he received no lasting burns and had not lost his eyesight. As well to everyone's amazement the rear mesh wall was gone, blown to bits along with the pot on the stove. We asked him, once he recovered, what happened. After putting out the small fire he inspected the inside of the stove and found a partially hidden old butane barbecue lighter that had caused the explosion. This was one event that could have been far more serious and we thanked God for keeping him safe.

I will not belabour this event, other than saying that during this year's trip we had no mishaps, cut feet, burnt hands, broken bones or bear attacks. That may sound astonishing in light of our history but we always remain thankful.

After a few days on the lake I decided to row down to the landing and start up the ATV and take it for a spin. I was happy to see no one had taken the bright green machine, and I proceeded to sit on it and pull the choke and push the starter button. No response. Nothing, so I checked all the connections and came to the wonderful conclusion that the battery had died. No problem, I would pull the starter cord. Here we go again, pull, pull, pull. No response. After a short rest I tried again, only pulling harder. On the third mighty pull I ripped a stomach muscle something awful. Now I not only had lost strength in my arms but the pain of pulling was too great to continue. At this point I gave up and headed back to camp. I decided not to burden my fair love with the latest news. I had no wish to revive the wrath of a woman already under stress from the memory of our trip in.

Two days later we saw a canoe come into view moving slowly. They came to shore and said hello. Two younger fishermen using an electric motor which I wished I had, asked how things were. I told them about my dilemma with the ATV and the one man said he would gladly pull the starter cord to get it going.

We left immediately before Mary had a chance to ask me what was going on.

The fellow was not only tall but strong, and in a few pulls the machine was running once again. I took it for a long spin to recharge the battery and was happy beyond measure and thanked the guys from the bottom of my heart.

One day later, we packed up our tents, sleeping bags and lawn chairs and stuffed what we could into the boat for our first return trip.

Once back at the landing, we unloaded the gear and then went up to start the four wheeler. You guessed it. The battery was dead as a doornail and my stomach had not healed enough to pull the cord in order to start it. That left but one option.

"Well, luv, let's leave all the stuff at the landing and go back to town and buy a new battery," I suggested. Mary seemed to like that idea and never said a word, which pleased me to no end.

My spirits however hit another low as I thought of the mile and a half walk back to the truck. The two men who had come in had told us of a bear around the area, and sure enough when we arrived, there was a huge pile of bear dung laced with a mixture of raspberry and blueberry sitting by the front door of the truck. I must say after some of the mishaps on our trip I expected the worst, like broken windows and who knows what. We found where the bear had left muddy prints on top of the fenders and hood and the glass as he peered in, but everything was intact. This had been a big bear and I was thankful there was no damage.

Nightmares sometimes come in packages, but often we overlook the many blessings we take for granted. Our truck started and away we went to town with the thought of buying a new battery. The store told us we would need to leave the new battery to be charged for a day, so we decided to return to Beach Lake. I phoned my chum Cris and told him of our problem, and he volunteered to bring out the new battery the following day. What a great guy. The old saying, "A friend in need is a friend indeed," holds true and with Cris he was always there to give a helping hand.

He has recently passed on to glory but will always be remembered as an example of a man who cared and helped others, and I miss him greatly.

We returned to the lake and spent the night at the campsite. Fortunately we had not taken the sleeping tent down, but we did have to bring back the propane stove and some food. The next morning found us rowing down the lake once again with the final load of gear and saying so-long to our fabulous beach.

Oh yes, some might ask if I had forgotten to bring back the spare tire from the house? Believe it or not I had remembered, so all I needed to do now was replace the rim and tire. Finally I had done something right.

Cris had arrived at the lake a short time before us and had put the new battery in. The day had started well. Poor Cris, without knowing what lay ahead he volunteered to help us make the trip out. I suggested he go home as we would do fine. By now it was noon hour and the day was hot and humid, with no wind, and hoards of deer flies and horse flies. The trip back to the truck would be a shade less than pleasant.

As we attempted to climb up the first rise with all its rocks and ruts, the 350 Yamaha with the overloaded cart refused to move. I kept accelerating and Cris and Mary pushed but sadly the machine lacked the power to pull us up the steep hill.

As he and Mary continued to push with all the strength they could muster, at the very moment I thought we were gaining ground, the ATV jumped high in the air going sideways, nearly throwing me off. The load would have tipped over if Cris had not kept it upright.

Once the machine settled down, I looked back at my wife who seemed to have a grin on her face.

"What's so funny?" I asked with my heart still beating faster than it should.

"When you landed, your eyeballs were the size of saucers," she replied. Cris had a twinkle in his eye that confirmed her statement.

Perseverance is a wonderful quality in life and so we kept on trying until we finally made it to the top.

My two hard workers were hot and tired already and we had only begun. I wouldn't have blamed them if they had gone on strike and deserted me.

The next hundred yards proved to be precarious, but we made it through the roughest section and headed down the trail, thumping and bumping our way in slow motion.

We had a few moments of grief along the way as we sunk in the ruts and swayed over the rocks and a few close calls where we almost lost the load.

At about the half way point I was sitting on the seat of the ATV taking a drink while I watched the two tired walkers walk closer.

"What's wrong now? You get tired of giving your butt a ride and decide to wait for us peasants?" Mary asked.

I considered that for a moment, and thought it best to head down the road without comment.

The trip with the first load took a long time, and we were exhausted by the time we arrived at the truck.

We tried not to think of the long trip back to the lake to retrieve the boat, motor and other equipment. That meant someone had to walk the mile and a half back through or around the mud holes and the rocks. I volunteered to go it alone with the ATV but Cris and Mary believed I needed help even though I assured them I could handle the twists and turns, the mud and boulders and anything else Murphy might throw my way. As it turned out they were right and I needed as much help as I could get.

As I think back on that trip, I am reminded of the toil and hardship the pioneers had to endure who took their life's possessions in the Conestoga wagons and travelled across the prairies. They and their families had to overcome the terrific heat of the day and the freezing cold of the night while sleeping in the great outdoors. What it must have been like to keep going through those weeks of danger and trouble I could never imagine. We had nothing to complain about, but I still did.

We eventually made it back to the lake, loaded and strapped the boat securely and began our trip back. All seemed to go well until we reached a spot in the road where I had to maneuver the boat around a tight corner. With the extra hands we tried to wrestle the whole contraption sideways so we could squeeze through. After several attempts we finally realized we would have to take everything out of the upright boat, untie it and lift it through the gap. A lot of extra work but nothing new for us on this trip. The question might be asked, how did we make it through on the way down and unable to on the way back. One of those unanswered questions we must leave to ponder at a later date.

By this time in our travel one might think it would be wise to take a rest but no, we plowed merrily on. We only had a short distance to the end of the roughest section and then we would have an easier time or so we hoped. We had barely retied the boat back down and reloaded it and started down the trail when disaster struck once more.

As I looked back to be sure everything was going well, one of the front tires on the ATV rode up on a large rock and the machine flipped over. I remember disengaging myself from the seat and flying through the air with the greatest of ease.

Fortunately I hit the ground rolling and the ATV missed me, even though the trail was slanted downhill. Another blessing to give thanks for.

Mary, who at the time was a few feet to the front, yelled back. "Are you ok?" Was that a note of concern I just heard? That was comforting, considering what I had put my dear wife through on this trip.

Cris, meanwhile was standing behind with a strange look on his face. "Whatever caused you to go over?" he asked, as he had not seen the cause of the flip over.

All three of us were quickly running out of steam so to speak but in a few moments we were able to set the ATV back on its wheels and straighten the load in the boat, which had not turned completely over.

After the last half mile of rocks, huge pools of watery mud holes and deep ruts, we finally staggered into the clearing where the truck sat. Well, at least my two companions arrived, staggering and exhausted with a look on their countenance I cannot describe.

The job of loading the boat up on the truck racks, storing the binneys and the gear inside the truck took a long time, and when you're tired it can seem even longer. As we were about to depart and head for home Cris made a comment I thought was a little premature considering Mary and I were still a year or two shy of receiving our OAS.

"You know, guys," he remarked solemnly, "I would suggest you consider your age from now on. These trips are getting far too hard."

At the time I didn't reply, as I am way to proud to admit anything like that. However in retrospect, Cris was the man who had warned me about bears on our camp road (that story can be found in a book called *North of the Soo*) and was a warning I didn't listen to and should have.

As I close this little tale of misery and woe, Mary and I have not gone back to our favourite beach for several years for various reasons. However, as the years have passed I think my sweetheart may be willing once again to attempt one more glorious camping vacation on that wonderful lake called "Beach Lake." "Shhhh, I won't remind her of the fun we had on the way in and out."

8. RETRIBUTIVE JUSTICE

Different folks at different times in the backwoods of Ontario, have experienced similar events, which is not unusual when we think of how many have challenged the great outdoors in the past two hundred years. As strange as it may be, part of the following events have been told in another story in this book that happened to totally different people. However as one of my favourite commentators on radio, Paul Harvey, would say, "now for the rest of the story." To that end I would encourage the reader to continue on and learn the reason for the title that has been used.

The afternoon sun was but a dim glow as two fishermen angled their canoe towards a shrouded shoreline near their campsite. The day had been overcast and cool with a slight breeze, making the temperature feel cooler than it really was. These men seldom took into account the new terminology known as wind chill factor. They simply put on more clothes and ventured forth. The time of year was mid May during the past century and global warming never entered their minds; in fact they probably wished May would be a whole lot warmer.

Far behind them two other men in a small fiberglass canoe were sitting in a peaceful looking bay casting to shore in hopes of catching trout. Life for the foursome had been good. They had survived the portaging and paddling to get to this lake, which was many miles from civilization. All the men were young, strong and eager to explore and fish the waters of Lake Superior Park where they now camped. Accidents and mishaps seemed to happen to others but seldom to them. They were wrapped securely in the eternal bliss of youth.

The campsite looked inviting to John, who sat in the stern and guided the craft to shore with smooth angled strokes. Dave, his partner in the bow, waited eagerly to disembark and head up to put on some tea and find some snacks. He was ravenous after spending the last few hours trolling around the lake and looked forward to stretching his limbs.

The crunch of small pebbles came to John's ears as he gave a strong pull on the paddle that sent the canoe sailing up onto solid ground. Dave stood up, stretched and stepped out of the canoe. As he often did he lifted the front of the canoe high in the air and reefed it further up on shore.

His head was bent forward when he heard a splash from the rear of the canoe.

Looking up he saw to his horror his friend floundering in three feet of water behind the canoe, holding onto a tackle box in one hand and a fishing pole in the other. Incredibly, as funny as the sight was of John standing in the water up to his waist, looking like a drowned rat, Dave was able to restrain himself from laughing out loud. The shock and disgust on the face of his fishing partner should have had him on the ground howling but to his credit he simply stood in disbelief. "What happened, John?" he blurted out.

"That's what I was about to ask you? Didn't you see me stand up and start to move forward in the canoe?"

Dave could only mouth a few words of apology and wait for John to come out of the freezing water.

The man slowly made his way through the shallow water and onto dry ground. His mind had returned to normal but strangely he did not utter a bad word. Dave, couldn't believe it, as his chum had been known in the past to have a foul temper and was even considered scary at times. Something had changed in this man's make-up.

"Are you hurt, pal?" he asked. "Can I help you?"

"No, get a fire going and I'll go change," John replied.

The pair hadn't noticed how much closer the other canoe on the water had come. They had no idea their chums, Rick and Chico, had witnessed the entire event, sending them into fits of hysteria. The two always enjoyed a good laugh especially if it was at the expense of their friends.

John immediately made his way to his tent where he had stored a small bag of spare clothes. Once he had changed into a dry shirt and pants and put on a dry pair of socks, he no longer was shaking from the dunking in the cold water. He exited the tent and began hustling around the fringe of the camp looking for sticks and branches to add to the fire Dave had already started.

As he scurried back and forth, he took note that his chum was using a small Swede saw and attempting to cut through a good sized limb hanging above his head. Looking back at the fire, John was about to throw more wood on when he heard an unearthly yell. Turning to look at the commotion, he could see Dave bent over holding his hand in a vice like grip.

"I think I just cut my thumb off," came a croaked whisper.

Stunned, John moved slowly across the open area to inspect the damage.

Grabbing a small towel hung on the clothesline, he came quickly alongside. Blood was flowing freely and covered his friend's hand and the sleeve of his jacket.

"Let me see how bad that cut is," John said as soothingly as possible. He reached out for Dave's arm but the man pulled away in fear of learning how bad the cut might be.

"Let me wrap that hand in this towel so we can stop the blood flow," John said in a raised voice.

Dave was looking at him and had a queer look on his face. "I can't look."

"What do you mean, you can't look?"

"I can't stand the sight of my own blood. I never could."

John was stunned. "What! Come on, we have to do this now! How could one of the great deer hunters of our time not stand the sight of blood?"

By now Dave was starting to shake a little, thinking about the accident. "No, I said I can't stand the sight of my own blood, not someone else's."

"Here, give me that hand," John rasped and grabbed Dave's wrist to take a look at the cut. At that moment Dave wobbled and began to sink to the ground.

"Things are going a little fuzzy," were the last garbled words he said before he passed out and John slowly lowered him to the ground.

Quickly he wrapped the wound tight with the towel, realizing it was far from being bacteria free, and then ran to get the first aid kit in his pack. On the way past the fire he made sure the water kettle was over the flame so they would have boiling water.

Once back beside Dave, he took out a swab bandage and cleaned the wound with warm water and alcohol and pinched the cut together as best he could. The man was stirring a little and had opened his eyes, staring off into space. John put a jacket under his head and watched him slowly return to consciousness while attempting to sit up. "Hang on, old fellow. Just sit there for a minute."

"Wow, I guess I passed out," Dave mumbled.

"Only for a moment or so," John replied as he finished putting a large bandage on the cut hand. "You'll be just fine, we won't have to carry you out on a stretcher." He laughed as he looked at Dave's pale face.

"How bad's the cut?" Dave asked.

"Well, the good news is you won't lose your thumb unless you get gangrene and then I'll have to take my trusty Puma knife and finish the job," John guffawed and gave his injured pal a big grin.

To end this story, Dave was able to finish the trip without further injury and probably never passed out again. His thumb did heal and he was far more careful using a saw thereafter. Whether or not he ever felt that the injury could be called retributive justice because he dumped his friend in the cold waters of Woodpecker Lake is unlikely. However, the other two who sat out on the lake still have a good laugh whenever they recall watching John take a flip backwards and later finding Dave nursing his cut thumb.

As for how well he controlled his temper when he found himself in the freezing water can only be attributed to his changed life he now lived in Christ.

9. A HEART POUNDING MOMENT

The Algoma Central Railroad winds its way through the forests that stretch from the city of Sault Ste. Marie to Hearst, Ontario passing alongside innumerable picturesque lakes and mind boggling scenery. As the train heads north it travels through several small communities like Searchmont, Hawk Junction, Dubreilville and Oba before arriving at the town of Hearst, the end of the line. Along the nearly three hundred mile route there are many mile markers where camp owners or fishermen can jump off.

Anticipation fills the heart of the eager outdoorsman whether they are planning a trip down the Agawa River or simply relaxing for a few days at their cabin. To those who spend time in the wilderness east of Superior, good times and thrills await in different forms. Following is a short story of a thrill that most would never wish to encounter.

Mile 77 was a crossing for a few years on the ACR that allowed the logging trucks to haul their logs across the tracks and down the 38 road to the mills in Sault Ste. Marie. The crossing was made from wood and made for a smooth passageway up and over the rails.

One day a few years past, a man called Eli and his friend John were making a trip to Eli's wilderness cabin situated on a small lake a mile from the crossing at mile 77. They planned to spend a few days fishing in the nearby lakes, cutting stove wood and watching for moose that loved to browse in the shallow lake nearby.

During these years a large population of moose inhabited this portion of the forest and whether a hunter or photographer, one could be assured of seeing a few moose. One of Eli's greatest joys was photographing the big animals as they stood in the shallows of the lake eating the grass and lily pads. His other enjoyment was eating moose meat, so each fall he would sit on his front porch with his trusty rifle in the hopes of bagging an animal.

There had been rumours over the years of this man from mile 77 being a proliferate bear killer. The story went that every time a bear broke into his cabin he would stay and wait for the marauder to return and then shoot it. It is told by some, and this is only a rumour, that at least five bear came and never left, so he became known as "ole bear killer." Now you might say that sounds a little cruel but if you had your property destroyed or you lay awake at night wondering if a bear was coming in...well, you might think differently.

However as this short tale resumes, the pair of campers are heading down the last stretch of the bumpy road that led from mile 80 to the crossing at mile 77. John drove his old faithful '74 Dodge pick-up loaded with supplies and equipment for the stay at the cabin. The old truck had seen far better days and that was being kind. To call it "old faithful" is another stretch of the true picture of the three-quarter ton 4X4 truck. This truck had been so abused by others that it would be difficult to find an area on it that did not have dents, holes or rust. And more importantly John had, on more than one occasion, crawled underneath in the mud or snow and replaced u-joints and other parts that had come loose.

However the old beast did have its good points. The truck was high and had big lug tires that worked well on the rough bush roads. As well he had put in a new engine and so hoped to keep it for some time.

As they approached the railroad tracks they saw to their dismay that the wooden crossing that had been in place during the spring was missing. John edged the front wheels up on the small grey stones that ran beside the tracks and stopped.

"The loggers must be finished hauling from this area, so the ACR took out the crossing," muttered Eli, looking intently ahead.

"I can jump those tracks easy," replied his friend. "This old truck has climbed over far worse things than that."

Eli looked up the tracks and took a look at his watch. "I'm getting out to listen for a train. It's nearly time for the tour train to be coming back from the canyon."

John sat for a moment and then climbed out of the cab. He went to the front wheels and turned the hubs, locking in the four wheel drive spindles. After climbing back inside, he put the shifter into gear. Leaning across the front seat he rolled down the passenger side window.

"Do you hear any sound of a train, Eli?"

"No, go ahead and get across. It won't be long before it gets here."

John stepped on the gas and slowly drove up on the closest rail. He knew jumping the tracks wasn't a good idea, but if they were to make it to camp they would need to do this.

The truck bumped over the first rail and moved across to the second one. Gradually he drove up on top of the next steel rail and then finally slid over. Unfortunately he had hit the gas petal too hard and the truck sprang far ahead and the front end dropped. He heard a strange noise from below his feet. Now the front wheels were over but the vehicle sat squarely across the tracks.

The old truck came to an abrupt stop. He gave it more gas and still it wouldn't move. He floored the old monster but could only hear the back tires spinning in the deep shale that ran beside the tracks.

"What's wrong now?" John grumbled to himself and stepped down from the cab.

Eli had walked fifty yards up the tracks, close to a bend in the railroad and hoped to slow the train down but realizing there was little hope of stopping the big engine in time. When he saw the truck spinning in the deep shale he began hiking back.

"There's something underneath the truck sticking down between the wood ties," he said pointing towards the middle of the vehicle.

John slowly lowered himself down on his knees and peered under the frame. Sure enough, he could see the problem. The u-joint that held one end of the four wheel drive shaft in place had broken loose, allowing the short drive shaft to swivel and fall straight down, embedding one end in the dirt between the ties. He managed to lie flat on his stomach and crawl under the truck on top of the wood ties. Grasping the steel shaft he reefed on the end stuck in the dirt. No movement. Turning his body a little he pulled with all his strength. The unit would not budge.

"Now isn't this a pickle we're in." Frustration edged the man's voice.

In the meantime Eli had bent down looking under the truck trying to think of a solution.

"You have to get the truck off the tracks and now!" he cried loudly as he stood upright. He was sure he had heard a noise from far up the tracks.

"What are you going to do?" he asked.

John was frantic. He knew the tour train would be coming any minute and here he was stuck in the middle of the tracks. Then he heard a double toot from a distance away.

"That's the train going past Batchawana Station, mile 80, do something quick, it'll be here in a few minutes!" Eli roared.

John's heart turned to stone as his mind raced. This was the worst dilemma he had ever been in. Should the train hit the truck, the train might come off the rails and with hundreds of tourists onboard, how many would suffer or die because of him. Then again, that would be the worst scenario; probably the locomotive engine would simply send the old truck flying off the tracks in a crumbled mass and no one would get hurt. He would be out a truck and have to pay a big fine. Great!

Quickly he jumped back in the cab and shoved the gas pedal to the floor one more time. The rear tires spun crazily sending small gravel flying for a hundred feet but the truck refused to move.

A sudden thought came to him. He climbed back out and ran to look in the box of the old beater.

Perhaps if he was able to jack up the rear of the truck, the broken drive shaft would loosen and if the back tires didn't spin out maybe they could still make it over the rails in time.

With great urgency he hauled out the big "Jack All" from the box of the truck along with a few pieces of wood. Running to the rear he flattened out a small area among the stones and put the jack under the bumper while sliding a flat board under the base.

"John! John! The train's almost here, I can hear it coming fast, only a mile away." His friend was yelling at the top of his lungs.

John's heart was pounding as he began to pump the jack handle. The lip held on the bottom of the bumper and he could see the back end begin to rise.

"Toooot!" the sound of a long drawn out whistle came to his ears as he furiously pumped up and down. The train was close to the corner where Eli stood. He slid some thick boards under both the rear tires and lowered the jack down. Running back to the open door of the truck he jumped in the cab. Looking out the passenger side window he could see his friend standing to the side of the tracks at the corner a mere fifty yards away.

Putting the truck into low gear he depressed the gas pedal with a short prayer. The last hope before disaster struck. Should the truck not move he would only have seconds to get out himself and move to safety. Once more he heard the loud blast of the train whistle as it came into the corner.

The old beat-up truck hesitated for a second and then sprang forward, bounding over the rails and down the other side of the tracks to the bush road. He glanced quickly up and saw the train coming towards him, already past where Eli stood. Five seconds later the tour train roared past, the tourists waving wildly without any idea of the danger he had put them in.

To close off this little tale, John learned that day to not take risks that might involve other people and was truly thankful the truck made it over. However he later surmised that God had one of his angels give that old vehicle a push with only seconds left before the train destroyed it.

PSALM 40

The A.C.R. Wilderness train

10. FOLLOWING THE TRACKS OF THE BLACK BEAR

Following is a collection of stories, some historical and some humorous that have been recorded over the years on the Algoma Central Railway (aka the Black Bear) and the settlements and lakes along the path.

Previous to the building of the ACR in the early 1900s there was no direct route to the town of Wawa that lay 140 miles north of Sault Ste. Marie. One could access the town by boating up Lake Superior or take a long circuitous route to the east; both could be not only time consuming but dangerous. The tracks of the Black Bear remained the only means of transport to the north till 1962 when Highway 17 North was finally completed through Lake Superior Park.

The ACR was incorporated in 1899 by a special act of the provincial government with the grand plan to join the CPR and carry on to Hudson Bay. As such, the first tracks were laid from the Helen Mines to Michipicoten harbour on Lake Superior in 1900 and it was named the Algoma Central and Hudson Bay Railway Co. in 1901. An agreement had been reached by the government and bondholders that one thousand male immigrants would move to the area each year for the next ten years. This might be considered a tall order and what jobs would they do? Presumably a large number of them would help build the railroad and others would be loggers or

167

work on the steam boats that would bring the iron ore from Michipicoten harbour in Wawa to the steel mill in Sault Ste. Marie. Consequently a steamship line was founded the same year.

Thus the serious construction of the railroad began in 1901 through wild untamed country by the pioneers as they hacked their way north.

Clearing the forest, levelling the land, filling in swamps and lastly building the trestles that would stand the test of time. Early pictures of some of the older trestles show how vulnerable they were and how the effects of nature often wiped them out during heavy rains and floods. Definitely a precarious time to be taking a train as they moved forward with the building of the tracks.

Interestingly, 1901 found the end of the tracks at Searchmont but by the end of 1902 they had reached Trout Lake and by the end of 1903 reached "Pangus Turn," mile 56. However it took another five years to reach mile 68, only a few miles short of Spruce Lake.

The reason for the dramatic slowdown was the financial collapse of the Clergue Empire in 1903, which included the money that funded the ACR.

During the days of early construction everyone had to be patient when on the train going north as it took five hours to reach the Pangus Turn or perhaps longer due to unforeseen circumstances. One slowdown for the train was the practice of stopping at one or more of the fresh water springs along the tracks. The engineer would usually stop the train at one of these springs on the way up and again coming down to fill up containers with cool clear water. These underwater springs bubbled up from below and in many cases left a cistern filled with fresh water, cold and clear. One such spring exists to this day a few yards north of mile 44 at Achigan Lake.

Another possible cause for the longer time on the train was the fact that the elevation rose from 510 feet at Achigan Lake to 1,453 at Mekatina crossing, a distance of a mere 18 miles, slowing the progress as the locomotive laboured up the incline.

ACTIVITIES ALONG THE TRACKS OF THE BLACK BEAR:

Many things could slow the train, and some of them are recorded for our amusement.

The new endeavour of building and maintaining a railroad was to be appreciated greatly by all those who wished to travel north and those looking for work. Although the majority of those taking advantage of the rails were men involved in logging and trapping, there were women as well.

Make no mistake that in the early 1900s women were treated as fragile pieces of humanity especially in the north unless you were a farmer's wife. Those dear ladies were of the same status as horses except they got to eat oatmeal while horses ate oats. However on the whole, women were put on a pedestal, which is understandable in the wild country as there were very few women. On one occasion the train backed up five miles in order to retrieve a lady's hat that had blown off when she stuck her head out the window. However it may have helped that the lady in question was a sweetheart of the conductor.

Interestingly, the women had their own car labeled "Women," at the rear of the train. Lumberjacks were placed in the front coaches and were deemed so rough that spiritually they were considered unsaveable. Many said that religious services were a waste of time as lumberjacks were destined for one place only. However, that did not stop clergy and missionaries from heading north to the lumber camps.

Other necessary slowdowns often occurred with the many stops to let passengers off that included men disengaging at logging camps and train workers who stopped to check rails or repair them. One story is told of a baggage man who had set up a floating barrel on Ogidaki Lake and every trip would have target practice from the moving car with his .303 Savage rifle. Of course we must assume the engineer would slow the train down so he would have more time to shoot.

During the early years, the wildlife was plentiful and the engineers kept a hand on the brakes and whistles constantly to avoid collisions. Passengers often were able to view the larger animals along the tracks as they stood nearby. Speaking of wildlife, one amusing event took place one winter day on the side of the tracks near Mongoose Lake, mile 75. As the story goes, the sun was incredibly bright, bouncing off the fresh overnight snow and the passengers were gazing out the windows taking in the beautiful scenery. The train was hurtling past the lake when many of the passengers were treated to a dazzling display of a pure white human backside not far from the tracks. One could honestly say the purpose was not for sunning but rather for "mooning" those going by. The folks aboard had no time to avert their eyes from the eye popping event, and the advice from the old song "Don't look Ethel!" was far too late.

Another funny story is told of the tourists and passengers gazing out the windows of the train as they rumbled slowly by Achigan Lake one sunny summer day fifty years ago. Through the years the ACR had installed telephone poles with crosspieces and strung the lines alongside the tracks so they could be used by workers, camp owners and various others. On this one occasion three enterprising teenagers had strung up a life sized mannequin by the neck that closely resembled a human being.

As the train came around the corner at mile 44 the tourists were busy snapping shots of the scenery, when suddenly the sight of someone being hung by the neck from the cross beam came into view. The crowning glory of the prank came as the three masked desperadoes were seen standing close by waving what appeared to be rifles. Needless to say there were a few screams and maybe even one lady passing out at the terrifying sight. In those days the locals found this very amusing but in today's world with the terrorism concerns we can only imagine the outcry. The engineer only smiled as the locomotive sped on down the track.

On the numerous lakes that lay close to the tracks there are many stories that abound. Trappers have some hair raising tales that definitely would make your blood run cold.

The men working on the tracks have their own set of tall tales, many of hardships and injuries. And of course there are the infamous lumberjacks who by all accounts worked far too many hours in either freezing cold or indescribable heat and the never ending blackflies and mosquitoes. Up at four a.m. and depending on the individual camp they ate a massive breakfast consisting of salt pork and beans smothered in molasses and if lucky a hunk of bread. Lunch time was short and once again pork and beans with prunes.

Supper time was usually eaten in the dark as the workers worked long hours and once again pork and beans sometimes with potatoes and bread. However there were a few camps closer to civilization that treated the workers on occasion with eggs, piles of sausages and pancakes along with gallons of coffee before heading out for a twelve hour day of chopping, sawing and clearing.

These hardy men were the initial group who cleared the forests to make way for our beloved ACR. We won't go into detail of their extra-curricular activities on their day off, which included events other than resting and reading. How much did a logger make a day in 1906? Hard back breaking work for a twelve to sixteen hour day grossed a man $1.00 a day. The all important cook received $50.00 a week, and the foreman managed $60.00 a week.

Many logging camps sprang up along the way on both the CPR and ACR lines and as the rails progressed so did the establishment of outfitting lodges and private camps.

COMPLETION OF THE TRACKS AND SOME FAMOUS PEOPLE WHO USED THE BLACK BEAR:

The building of the Montreal River trestle at mile 91 1/2 was completed by October 1911. The trestle was 1,550 feet long and 130 feet high with the longest span of 85 feet and other spans of 75 feet each. This would be one of the engineering feats that would amaze the travellers as well as put fear in the hearts of the more nervous as the train rattled over the new structure.

During the year of 1912 the tracks reached Hawk Junction, mile 165, and meant a huge distance had been covered in one short year.

Six months later the new tracks crossed the CPR tracks at Franz, mile 195, and the CNR tracks at Oba, mile 245. A short six months after that the rails made it to Hearst, a significant accomplishment overall considering the terrain.

Special mention of former thriving communities would be Mosher, mile 217, which now is nearly abandoned, and Oba, mile 245, which has slowly lost many of its residents.

By 1914 the track was completed to Hearst, mile 296, and the Black Bear cancelled further expansion to Hudson Bay and in 1965 dropped any reference to the Hudson Bay Co. and was thereafter called the Algoma Central Railway.

Some interesting data records three of the Group of Seven artists, J.E.H. MacDonald, Lawren Harris, and Frank Johnston renting a box car refitted as a cabin for a month as they painted along the line from Batchewana to Agawa Station from 1918 to 1923. In the fall of 1921 they were joined by A.Y. Jackson and Arthur Lismer to paint and sketch from the Eton area to Sand Lake. Nearing the end of summer, Jackson and Lismer continued on up the ACR to Franz where they caught a CPR freight to Schreiber and walked to Rossport on the road that followed Lake Superior.

There are many stories that are attached to the railway and of the numerous settlements that sprang up during the early 1900s close to the tracks. Logging was prolific during these years, and both spruce and pine trees were heavily harvested and sent down the rivers wherever the tracks were built. Many small communities grew and land opened up for farmers as well as the loggers. Logs were sent down many of the rivers flowing into Lake Superior such as the Goulais, Montreal, Batchawana, Agawa and Michipicoten rivers.

Numerous small logging camps sprang up close to the waterways and pulp wood was loaded on the flat cars from 1901 and on.

Noteworthy as well were the huge log booms of pulp-wood of up to four thousand cords near the shores of Lake Superior close to the rivers where the logs had been sent down. The loggers using cant hooks and pike poles risked their lives on the river booms to keep the logs from jamming up. Balancing themselves on the turning logs in the water, they became very adept at jumping and running from one log to another. Unfortunately some were lost or injured when their spiked boots lost grip and they fell between the logs. Once out on the big lake, tug boats would haul these massive booms to the wood mills.

THE TALE OF TWO TOWNS AT THE END OF THE ROAD:

The turn of the century brought excitement and hopeful-ness to the area north of Sault Ste. Marie. Two settlements to be known as Searchmont and Wabos had begun to blossom in 1901 with the railway stretching twin rails towards the town of Hearst far to the north. Logging and homesteading was on the rise and prosperity beckoned those who were willing to work hard and endure the rigours of the outback.

And so it was the small community of Searchmont sprang up during the late 1800s and really began to grow in 1901 when the new tracks were finally laid. The area bus-tled with activity and from 1899 to 1901 as the Algoma Commercial Co. and the Hope Lumber Co. operated lumber camps and a sawmill situated at the end of the Hult Road and Glendale. The town was named after T.C. Search, treasurer of the Lake Superior Pulp and Paper Co. during these early years. A group of men from United States that included T.C. Search, Mead, Harrisburg, Talbot and Francis H. Clergue had formed the company and hired a great number of lumberjacks to cut hardwood, spruce, pine and other trees that could be used for lumber, charcoal and paper. The Standard Chemical Co. of Canada built 26 charcoal kilns near the present day ski hill in 1928. They only lasted a few years.

One interesting side line in 1903 was when the company ran out of money and could not pay the loggers. This became a serious time in the life of the little town. A brand new hotel had been built to accommodate train passengers and other visitors and stood as a testimony of the earnestness of the developers and owners of the logging business. Regardless, the lumberjacks were not a group to mess with. Because of all the new development, which included a new hotel, houses, train station and sawmills, sabotage was a definite threat. Consider for a moment if only one disgruntled logger decided to tear up a few feet of track. What a disaster that would be! History has recorded that sabotage of this nature took place quite often during this time period in United States.

After a great deal of rumblings and threats, the loggers finally rioted in the nearby town of Sault Ste. Marie and one can only imagine the fear and trepidation that spread through the small community of Searchmont. To resolve this dilemma, the Ontario government stepped in and paid the lumberjacks the money owed them.

Another interesting tidbit in 1903 showed disagreement between F. Clergue and J. Gaudette and H. Huckson over the placement of a brand new large sawmill.

Clergue had recently formed the Lake Superior Pulp and Paper Co. and disagreed with the decision by the others to build the mill on the south side of the Goulais River south of the bridge. The mill ended up being built north of the bridge where it stood till it shut down in 1980. The old structure remained on site till its demolition in 2013.

A new hotel built in 1903 came to be known as the "White House" and was sold in 1906 to Peter and Hilda Sundstrom for the grand total of $4,900.00. They owned the building for the next fifty years and sold it in 1956 to the Grahams who put in plumbing, water, heat and eventually power. Unfortunately the White House was destroyed by fire in October 1973 and never rebuilt.

By 1914 Searchmont had grown to a population of 500 residents. A short five miles away the settlement of Wabos had grown to ninety families. Life was abuzz in the remote area.

Records state that the first good dirt road to make it all the way to Searchmont was finally completed in 1924 and the first automobile to make it all the way from Highway 17 was driven by Charlie Pellinon and L. Maki in 1926. The new road was curvy, rough and often washed out by spring and fall rains. The previous road had ended at Island Lake. A single lane bridge was built in 1920 across the Goulais River made with steel railings and a wooden bottom. The current bridge was not built till the late 1970s. Up until then the only access to the town was by rail. Should you wish to cross the river by foot you had to walk the tracks, which was viewed as trespassing by the train company.

In the beginning the south side of the river was named Goulais and the north side called Searchmont. Eventually they were to become one name. The road was not paved till 1966 and the school buses had to travel 36 miles on a dirt road each day to take the children to high school in Sault Ste. Marie. A somewhat precarious trip at any time of the year driving through snow, sleet, rain and muddy conditions on a winding road.

Electrical power was not installed in the town till 1962 at the cost of $153,000 to cover the 36 miles from Bellevue. Several folks are still alive in the community that can tell of the advent of the new lights being installed in their homes.

Life during these years was rugged and difficult and yet the families were true pioneers and have left a great heritage.

Following is a story of the settlement five miles north of Searchmont and one individual who was raised there.

THE STORY OF ONE SMALL TOWN AND ONE BIG MAN:

The community of Wabos is some five miles north of Searchmont. We have been told it was named from the native word for rabbit. The early beginnings of this area really blossomed in the early 1900s with the cutting of the spruce trees for pulp and the opening of the parcels of land for homesteads from 1907 to 1920. Extensive cord wood camps sprang up throughout the entire region. The logs were used for making charcoal, a black form of carbon produced by partially burning wood in large kilns from which air was excluded.

As the tracks began to reach north, the loggers would load the cord wood on the flat cars and have it sent southward and the days of floating the logs down the Goulais river and the Achigan Creek came to an end. The last pine log drive in this area was 1910 down Achigan Creek.

Many of the first immigrants in the Wabos area were

177

Finnish with a few Scots who bought land for home-steading from the Crown known as Sirvico property.

Gradually over the years from 1911 to 1930 the Finlanders bought up most of the property sold by the railway company and the Scots seemed to fade away. The settlement of Wabos began to grow as the loggers' camp at mile 38, known as Neimi's Finnish Logging Camp, pros-pered with a cookhouse, a blacksmith shop, a stable, a foreman's shack and various other buildings.

Bill Autio, who still resides in Wabos, remembers spending time in the oldest building owned by the cord wood company and later by Hulda Autio, his grand-mother. Hulda and her husband were the first Finnish immigrants to this area. In 1920 she moved to Wabos and opened a Finnish co-op store in their home, which was open till 1932. A hard-working lady, she was the post-mistress and ACR station agent from 1927 till 1952.

Children were present in the area but it would appear the first school was in a house till 1922, when a new school house was built. The first community centre was raised in 1928. All this activity blossomed with the building of the railroad facilitating the logging industry and the buying up of the land for homesteading.

Until the building of the Algoma Central Railway in 1900, first to Heyden and then heading north to Searchmont, there was little access to this remote region.

The first known road connecting Wabos to Searchmont did not exist till 1924 and the first bridge made from wood crossed over Achigan Creek and was not built till sometime in the twenties. By 1934 a new, much better bridge was built.

There was a path for those inclined to walk the six miles to Searchmont in the pre-1920s from Wabos and a trail of sorts connecting Heyden to Searchmont as well did exist in the early years.

In 1950 Ahti Autio, a resident of Wabos and father of Bill, took a job as a Forest Ranger and lived for three years in a cabin on Trout Lake, mile 56 on the ACR with his wife and son. Several cabins had sprung up near the tracks where they lived. On one particular day, little Bill and his chum saw smoke rising not far across the lake and so rowed over to see what was going on. No one was around and they could see flames and smoke which put fear in their hearts so they rowed like crazy back across the lake to tell his mother. She was able to contact Bill MacKay, the local Fire Ranger by the old style battery phone in their house. The Fire Ranger could then send word by another phone to his supervisors and get permission to leave his perch on the Ogidaki fire tower and travel back the seven miles to Trout Lake to inspect the fire.

Bill MacKay's job each morning was to ride his BSA125 motorbike along a roughly cleared trail to the Ogidaki Fire Tower, spend the day alone watching the surrounding forest for fires and then return at night back along the trail.

Perhaps the comical part of this whole story would be that the local Soo newspaper took photos of Bill's mother and told of her bravery in preventing the fire and left out the real hero, a little five year old boy who had discovered the fire and told his mom about it.

Once she knew about the fire, she took her son and his friend in their little skiff back across the water to see if they could put out the fire themselves. The newspaper clippings along with photos extolling the courage acts of Bill's mom can still be found and the boy, now a man, can relate first hand what went on that day. Fire Ranger MacKay arrived and the fire was extinguished and all ended well.

Little Bill Autio was to spend three years on the lake before his family moved back to Wabos.

His father, a tall, strong, hard working man weighing two hundred and forty pounds drove truck and trapped but sadly passed away early in life at the age of forty from an unusual disease peculiar to Finlanders—*polycystic lipo membranous osteodysplasia with sclerosing leukoence-phalopathy*. For obvious reasons most Finlanders call it a polycystic disease!

Bill's mother lived in Wabos till she reached 90 years of age in 2010 when she passed on.

Bill attended a small one room schoolhouse at the end of the road that accommodated grades one to eight through the '50s. During those years he grew in size and often walked the six miles to Searchmont and enjoyed diving off the new bridge built over the Goulais River. (Hopefully his mother did not hear of these exciting adventures.) He greatly relished the times when his mother would take him on a walk down the road to shop at the country store run by Ernie Latinen. The store was a going concern and was situated nearly a mile away on what is now Highway 532 and was open till 1955. The young man enjoyed all the items displayed including a variety of tools, farming equipment, clothing and all sorts of food. These were good days for the children, especially with the advent of the power lines in 1962. Once the electricity was hooked up they were able to put away the coal oil lamps and see things in a different light, so to speak.

During the 1970s Bill began to excel in power lifting and competed in weight lifting contests around the country. Possibly the strength of his father was handed down through the genes as Bill lifted massive weights, setting records in the heavy weight division as he now had grown to be a very strong man.

Much more could be said in these pages about the Finnish immigrants and their offspring and others who endured the hardships of those early years, working hard and prospering. A rich heritage indeed and we give tribute to each one from these two settlements.

The hills of Achigan

11. RARE TALES FROM ACHIGAN LAKE

On many of the lakes of the north, there are stories that have been passed down through the years. Some of these stories can be scary, some unusual but most are amusing. Camp owners and those that visit them often become involved in strange incidents that are never recorded or told verbally for various reasons. Hopefully the reader will enjoy these true to life stories from Achigan Lake compiled from a rich and diversified past.

Achigan Lake is named from the French Canadian "d'achigan a grande bouche," derived from the Algonquin name "At-Chi-Gane" meaning "bass" or "fighter." How long the bass in Achigan have been there no one knows. Some claim that the French Canadians in early years brought them to Canada. With the coming of the railroad it became necessary to put a berm across part of the lower south end along with a concrete tunnel allowing water to flow through. This became the only access point by water from what became known as Lower Achigan to the upper and larger portion known as Upper Achigan Lake. The tracks would wind around the corner and over this section as it moved along the edge of the lake to mile 44.

The combined enterprise known as Algoma Steel and the Algoma Central Railway with a dozen holdings originally was a vision of the U.S. industrialist Francis Clergue between the years 1892 and 1903. He watched a frontier outpost called Sault Ste. Marie grow from 2000 to 8500 people with a steel mill, a pulp mill, two railways, two power companies and a fleet of steamships.

In the next few years the enterprise decided they wanted a lodge on one of the lakes close to the train tracks. Some of those in leadership began to travel the rails in search of the best location for a good sized lodge. The search took some time but finally all were agreed the two long sandy beaches at the north end of Achigan Lake were ideal. The property covered one hundred and eighty acres of mixed forestland, marshlands and hills.

The construction of the lodge began as early as 1920 and was completed by 1923 using large white pine logs from the property with most of the construction done by the capable hands of Finnish carpenters. A separate log cabin built close to the large lodge was erected as well. Another cabin built from left over logs was erected some distance south on the west side of the lake and there our first story begins.

Told to the author by an old camper of great integrity who has passed on to glory, I will hopefully keep the words as close as possible to his narration.

During the middle of the 1900s, several Roman Catholic priests began to regularly stay at the log cabin on the west side of the lake. Two of the priests often had friendly competitions in growing vegetables and other garden delectables hoping to grow the most or the biggest. Their rousing competitions in games and crafts became the gossip of the lake. Father Brennan was a large man who enjoyed taking his ten foot skiff and rowing around the lake several times a week. He often would take a passenger for company being an affable man, usually one of his neighbours or on occasion, one of the nuns who stayed at the cabin at the far end of the lake close to the railroad tracks. The nuns had been coming for retreats to this cabin for many years. Many old timers who have long since left us have said this was the first cabin built on Achigan Lake.

The two men who became the most well known were Father Brennan and Father Murphy. Father Brennan retired during the 1950s and decided to live on Achigan Lake year round in the log cabin built some thirty years prior by the Finnish carpenters. This gentleman had been a priest for a long time and was in his late sixties by most accounts. Definitely a challenge for anyone of any age he was not only older but in poor physical condition. However that did not deter him in the least and he made his plans during his first summer on the lake and prepared for the winter to come. One of the first things he did was to cordon off part of the inner cabin where the woodstove sat and set up a small area for eating, sleeping and reading. Next he began to cut smaller trees and drag them to the cabin where he used a Swede bucksaw to cut them into stove lengths.

Day in and day out he swung his axe and sawed his way through many trees, stockpiling several cord of wood for the cold winter ahead. Relentlessly he laboured on, not only bringing in wood but making a sleigh to haul water from the lake and compiling all the necessary items he would need to survive the winter.

Food was needed and what was he to do? True he could catch the train and ride out to the city for some of the staples including veggies and fruit but on the whole he would need to either bake or fry things like bread and sweets. Once the ice froze over he would be able to ice fish as there was an abundance of lake trout in the lake; however what he really needed was good solid red meat.

In the month of September he cleaned an old 303 British Enfield rifle and took some target practice near the cabin.

Using his compass one day in October he headed across the railway tracks and up through some marsh lands. He knew that by himself the shooting of the moose would be the easiest part of the endeavour. During the next couple of weeks he quietly scoured the bush near his camp looking for the elusive beast, making a few calls in the evenings and waiting patiently near an old animal trail. Then unexpectedly, one frosty morning as he silently moved through a cedar swamp he came across a big cow. She was taking a drink from a slough of brackish looking water and did not seem to notice his presence. The beast was only a few hundred yards from his dwelling, so with a steady hand and a good eye he dropped the animal on the spot.

The work of cutting up the quarters and transporting them through the bush was a difficult job for any man and especially for an older man who had never done any hard physical labour. Perseverance and necessity will make a man like Father Brennan work harder than he could ever imagine. Consequently after all the physical work around camp, carrying water, chopping and sawing several cords of wood and living sparsely he had lost his body fat and was now lean and hard. In only a couple of days the priest hauled the moose to camp and cut it up, smoked some of the meat and seasoned the rest in preparation for the long winter ahead.

The winter finally came, cold and long but the man endured and even enjoyed the time spent on the shores of Achigan Lake. On occasion a fellow priest or a friendly camper would drop by for a social call that was always a bright spot in his day. When he felt the pangs of loneliness creeping upon him he would take his snowshoes and visit other camps. In the summer there were far more people on the lake and they would often drop around to talk. Sadly, one warm evening Father Brennan was to pass on to his great reward in heaven. We give a tribute to a man who had the courage and fortitude to live out his dream of solitude on a remote lake.

12. A BOY NAMED ROBB

At the southwest corner of Achigan Lake there still remains an old dilapidated building that at one time had been a bustling outfitters lodge called Achigan Lake Camp. The camp came into being some time after the railway was built and the clients were mostly fishermen and hunters. Although the paths and trails that were cleared during those early years are long overgrown, they once led to many of the surrounding lakes in the Achigan area.

The lodge owner was J.A. Mantyla and family and they ran a true wilderness outfitting fishing camp. They leased boats and canoes and had canoes on all the small lakes in the area west of Achigan. Fishing was fabulous during this period, and included grey trout, bass, pike and brook trout. The family had put in hours and hours of work to run the trails to these lakes. Fisherman were welcome to stay for $7.00 per day for meals and lodging. A fishing and outdoor paradise indeed and one that we can only dream about in these days. Are there any misty tales or ghostly remnants that might still remain? One young boy was to find out.

Our story begins one cloudy warm day during the month of July, a long time ago. A mother and her two children decided to take a stroll in the bush behind the old camp.

Robb was barely in his teens and very inquisitive and perhaps a shade hyperactive. His sister, being two years older, was a quieter, more reserved youngster. As they disembarked from their boat on the shore they grabbed their lunches and small tins for collecting raspberries. The blackflies had died down by this time in July and the mosquitoes only came out in the evenings so they all felt they wouldn't be molested. Perhaps they should have been concerned of black bears but for some reason the threesome had no fear of wild things.

The family headed up the embankment and onto the train tracks that wound along the shore of the lake, listening carefully for the sound of an oncoming train They knew the tour train was not due till 3 p.m. and the train from Hearst two hours later. The freight trains usually ran through the night.

The young family took their time walking up the long grassy grade that led to the first building. They edged closer to what they assumed was the property line on the south side in order not to disturb anyone but could see no one at home. They felt confident the folks wouldn't mind if they crossed the property in search of old trails, such was the friendliness of the camp owners on the lake.

In a short time they reached the back part of the property and were making their way past an old abandoned cabin when Robb made a bee-line for an opening in the dwelling where an old weather beaten door hung by one hinge.

"Robb, don't go in there!" yelled the mother.

"I just want to look in," he replied over his shoulder as he pushed through a tangle of raspberry bushes that tore at his bare arms and legs.

"Stay with us. You can't see anything in the long grass, there might be sharp things all over."

The boy's mother and sister began to carefully pick their way through a host of brambles with sharp needles heading towards the remains of a large camp. In the meantime Robb had stepped inside the dark interior and stood still, waiting for his eyes to adjust before moving forward. Already in his young life he had been criticized for being impatient and too willing to run ahead without taking precaution. Taking a few steps he carefully scanned the old floor boards waiting for his family to arrive. He was eager to explore the inside of the old building.

"Come out of there, now!" came his mother's voice.

"I can see some old stuff lying around, Mom, and it's really neat in here."

His mother was now standing in the doorway peering into the dark interior. She heard the old floorboards creak ominously as the boy moved to the centre of the camp.

"Don't go any further, there's holes in the floorboards and the roof is half collapsed."

"Aw Mom, I see something in the corner. I want to see what it is," came the reply.

Parents know what happens when impatience and curiosity are combined in a youngster, usually something disastrous. She took a step inside in order to see her son but the interior was enclosed in a strange form of opaque light. "Come out now, I won't tell you again."

The room had a strong, damp, mouldy smell that affected her breathing. If only she had a brought a handkerchief to put over her mouth.

She could barely make out a mess of decaying debris scattered about on the floor.

"I'm coming out Mom, but I see a pile of stuff in the corner and what looks like a big toy."

His eyes had adjusted to the darkness and he could see broken furniture strewn about with rotting clothes littering the inside of the room.

Suddenly he stopped dead in his tracks. Straining his eyes he thought he saw movement. Something big and black with what appeared to be two yellow eyes. The sound of a heavy chain being dragged along the floorboards and a metallic rattle came to his ears.

"Ma! What was that?" he turned to question her. Curiosity had turned quickly to fear. He stood in a petrified state without moving. Perhaps his overactive imagination and too many ghost stories came into play.

"I have no idea, but there's the sound again. Maybe a bear or wolf is tangled up in a chain or is caught in a trap," Mary suggested and wished her husband was there.

Robb had slowly moved towards her and without a sound he began to run. Through the open door, past his sister he ran as if the demons of Hades were on his tail. Never looking back he headed for the railroad tracks and the boat on the shore. Forgetting entirely about his mother and sister, his fear overcame him and he left them to deal with the unknown element inside the cabin.

The young man made it to the boat and there he was found by his mother and sister sometime later. No amount of persuasion could move him from his seat. He refused to go for a walk past the building and only wished to go home.

Things that move in the darkness, strange sounds coming from unknown sources can be far scarier to a youngster than real danger in the sunlight. He knew he hadn't been really courageous, but he didn't care.

He felt better when he recalled how his dad at the same age had been scared out of his wits. Sitting on the top rail of a cedar fence that separated the back field from the woods, his father was resting with his .22 calibre rifle on his lap. Night was approaching fast and the bush behind was clothed in darkness but the open field to the front of him was still light enough that he would be able to find his way home.

Suddenly in the quiet of the evening came the loudest, most horrible scream he had ever heard, from right behind where he sat; an unearthly piercing cry that raised the hair on the back of his neck and put absolute fear in his heart. He jumped from his perch and with great urgency headed for home as fast as his young legs could carry him.

Some folks later surmised it was only a bobcat his father had heard but for Robb, even knowing his dear old dad had a similar experience, made him feel a whole lot better.

The following day the young man decided to take a bicycle ride on the logging road behind their camp. He had heard that the trucks were done hauling as the company was finished in the area and would be gone shortly. His bicycle had fat 20-inch tires and he loved the challenge of whipping down the dirt road, hitting the bumps and flying down the hills. One long hill in particular thrilled him, with lots of bumps and a steep section.

He never wore a helmet, simply for the reason during those years no one did. On this day he failed to tell his parents that he was going for a bike ride. Perhaps a recipe for disaster but that never entered his mind and by the time anyone missed him who cared.

Robb knew of a road that led far up into the back country. One arm would take him close to Ogidaki Lake and the other arm right past a smaller lake he knew his dad had fished. Going up some of the hills could be tough but coming down them at a wild, reckless speed was unbelievable fun.

The only thought in the young man's head was having fun and going fast. Far from his mind was the potential danger of accidents or encounters with animals or trucks. As he sped around a bend on the road he suddenly jammed on his brakes, the rear tires skidding wildly, throwing gravel stones across the road. Going into a desperate slide his heart pounded wildly at the sight in the centre of the road. Standing in the middle blocking the way was the biggest black bear he had ever seen. He had seen a few bears but this one was definitely big.

The bike slid closer and closer and the boy hung on, desperately hoping to stop before he hit the animal.

His left knee dragged on the ground cutting through his skin to the bone on his knee cap, but he felt no pain so intense was the moment of panic. At the last moment before impact the bear lunged forward and into the bush. Robb and the bike now laid flat slid through the spot where the bear had stood. Only a second separated the two from colliding and no one knows what may have happened had the bear not moved. Robb turned his bicycle around and headed home, his legs still shaking from the close encounter. His parents told him later it is not unusual for one to shake after such a moment.

The family still gives thanks to the Lord for the safety of their son. How remarkable that in the space of a couple of days the teenager would have two experiences that would send the adrenalin through his young body that he would not feel again for some time.

A LONG WINTER'S WALK:

Robb was to have one more experience that would cause him grief; such was his luck or destiny as he grew older. One weekend at the age of nineteen he asked Cathy, his girlfriend at the time, to come up to Achigan Lake for a visit to the family cabin to spend the day. They would take a forty five mile train ride on the Algoma Central Railroad from Sault Ste. Marie and walk across the ice, the time being late February and the ice well frozen.

He was proud of the look of the refurbished cabin with its pine cove siding and new front porch. His parents and he had worked hard to build a larger building in a setting with a small creek and a good beach.

His girlfriend had voiced some doubts as she had to be at work that evening by 8 p.m. and had been told the train usually did not arrive back in the city till 6 p.m. which would not give her much time to prepare for work. Robb in his usual manner had been able to persuade her to come anyway.

The day had begun full of hope and excitement as they watched the beautiful scenery from the big windows in the train car. The sunlight made the day seem very special as it highlighted the snow on the trees and landscape. They were thankful the day was not extremely cold and they had been told the snow and ice had settled and was hard packed, which would make the walking much easier going.

The young people were happy and Robb's girlfriend felt better and put her concerns of work and the return trip out of her mind. As the train rounded the shores of Achigan Lake the long drawn out sound of the train whistle came to

195

their ears. They made their way to the unloading steps and jumped out into the snow bank. Waving to the conductor the train sped away heading for the next lake called Ogidaki.

Robb and Cathy followed a beaten path in the snow past a camp and down onto the lake. A day without a storm or wild wind was a bonus for the couple, especially crossing a lake where the wind could drop your body temperature in minutes if you weren't dressed properly. The two hikers were dressed in jeans and light jackets with no long johns, which usually is not recommended outdoor gear. Looking cool was far more important than warmth to these two city dwellers.

The pair hurried across the lake and were soon warmed by the radiant heat from the big wood stove in the cabin. They spent a fun day ice fishing, drinking hot chocolate and eating goodies and keeping an eye on the clock so they wouldn't miss the train that would take them home to the Sault.

The train was scheduled to pass Achigan Lake at 3 p.m. but was notoriously late, sometimes over an hour or more.

As the day wore on, the couple prepared to walk back across the lake. At 2:45 p.m. they realized they should already be at the waiting spot so they hurriedly said their good-byes and began their hike back across the lake. The weather had been sunny all day and the warmth and relaxing time perhaps slowed them and it was exactly at 3 p.m. they heard the train whistle a short three miles away. Robb and his girlfriend were only a hundred yards from shore and a short two hundred feet from there to the train stop as they began to run.

The train travelled the three miles from Ogidaki Lake in record time and with only a hundred feet to go to the tracks, the young pair watched as the cars sped by. They had missed the train! All hope was lost as the train was the only way to get home. Distraught and frantic, Cathy began to weep. What could they do? She had to be at work by 8 p.m.

She sat down on the tracks and tried to regain her composure. Robb had to decide whether to walk back to camp for the night or start hiking down the tracks toward Searchmont a mere thirteen miles away.

They were young and strong and the decision was made to walk the tracks to Searchmont and then hopefully someone would be able to come and pick them up. Unfortunately for Cathy, her legs were short and not as strong as her boyfriend's but that did not change their decision and off they went.

Back at camp, Robb's parents had seen the train race past the lake and knew in their hearts the couple had not made it in time. They also wondered at the turn of events as the train was always late, not early. Today however it had been a shade early and now the parents waited for the young people to return. After an hour they came to the conclusion they weren't coming and must be hiking down the railroad tracks.

Meanwhile, the pair of young people had begun their walk to Searchmont. At first all seemed fine with the sun still shining in the afternoon blue sky and the fresh legs of youth taking two wooden ties at a time, they strode confidently forward.

However after the first hour of hiking and watching the day beginning to darken with the sun gradually descending in the west the reality of their situation became far more real. Mile 42 on the tracks appeared ahead and they could see the old station house from years past sitting quietly in the approaching shadows of the day.

A small bench welcomed them to take a rest. For a few minutes they sat quietly without a word and then suddenly Cathy broke out sobbing. Robb didn't know what to do.

He finally asked her what was wrong and she told him, she was already tired out and knew she couldn't make it another ten miles. That meant two things: first was the danger of spending a night in the bush, which they could not survive and second, any hope of making it to work in time was gone. He tried to comfort her at first but she continued to cry, feeling all was lost with no hope. Eventually with much persuasion he convinced her to try walking again as the cooler evening air was descending and their jackets and trousers were far too light to keep them warm. He also realized their running shoes were not warm enough to keep their feet from freezing.

Sometime later the couple passed the mile 38 marker. The scenery along the way had been breathtaking as the tracks followed the meandering Achigan Creek with the snow covered conifers close by. At this point even Robb was tiring a little and he wondered if Cathy would make it. Surprisingly she had kept up her speed and had taken only one short rest. Neither one spoke as they trudged along and he wondered what thoughts were going through her mind. He decided he needed to communicate something to her as they still had miles to go, at least six miles he calculated.

"How are you doing, darling?" he blurted out. "Do you want to rest or do you think we should keep going?"

"My legs feel like stumps, and I need to sit down," came the answer.

"Yeah, I'm tired too. Say, there's a cement causeway just ahead where we can sit for a few minutes."

Darkness had descended on the forest as they agreed to give one last push in the hope of making Searchmont before the local restaurant closed at 8 p.m. That would be their last chance to phone a friend from the Sault to pick them up. He pulled his girlfriend to her feet and looked into her eyes. What he saw gave him a small ray of hope. Thankfully she was not as despondent as she was earlier and he saw a flicker of determination in her eyes. Perhaps they could finish their trek. There was no alternative, already he could feel the cold air closing in around them. Who could tell how cold the night would be. Keep moving was his only thought.

In a short time they could see lights like diamonds sparkling in the moonlight a mile away. Of course, he thought with a sigh of relief, that's Wabos and I could ask someone if I could use their phone. He conveyed his thoughts to Cathy who seemed almost on the verge of collapse. To his amazement and without hesitation she said no.

"How far to Searchmont, is it?" she asked.

"Around 5 miles."

"Let's walk the rest of the way. I'm a little nervous of strangers," she mumbled.

Robb could hardly believe his ears. If he was zonked how must she feel. Amazing! Down the tracks they went. How many cross ties had they passed over he wondered. Walking the rails certainly wasn't a cake walk.

One and a half hours later the two totally worn out teenagers arrived in the small hamlet of Searchmont and staggered into the restaurant that was closing up for the night. The time was exactly 8 o'clock! They had somehow made it in time. The owner looked them over and felt pity for the two bedraggled kids and cooked up two big juicy hamburgers. Robb meantime phoned his friends in the city and asked if they would come and pick them up.

There's an old saying that goes something like this. "All's well that ends well." That's usually true to a point. Then again there's always an aftermath as there is to this story. The long winter hike had no lasting physical affects on the determined couple; however emotionally Robb was to find out it is never a good thing to take a girlfriend on a hike she didn't expect to have. She not only missed work but she dropped her boyfriend like a hot potato, and who could blame her.

13. AN ODD MOMENT ON THE OLD GROWTH FOREST TRAIL

Situated in the hills southwest of Little Achigan Lake is a section of forest that has been designated as Old Growth Forest primarily due to the efforts of a man known as Jeff Hinich from Wabos and the agreement with the Ministry of Natural Resources over twenty years ago. Within this small area there are several massive white pines over three hundred years old. Interspersed with the pines are a few extremely large yellow birches of unknown age and one fallen cedar tree of a size no one may ever see again.

Two men and two women wound their way up a steep little path that paralleled a small stream.

Eventually the path would lead to the Old Growth Forest. The day was hot and muggy as the four hikers slowly climbed upward. This was the first time Richard and Paulette had been on the narrow trail and they followed silently behind their friends John and Mary. Richard, who enjoyed his friends calling him Dick, had heard them mention the huge trees and looked forward to the excursion.

The two couples came out into a large area with a small lake in the centre and long yellow grass growing around the perimeter.

"John, is this what they call Minnow Lake?" Paulette queried, as she moved along the edge of the water.

"Yes, Jeff told me that for the past fifty years or more the fishermen have left minnow traps here and always caught lots of minnows."

"Where do we go now? I don't see the trail?" Dick asked.

"We move around the edge of the water, circumvent half of the lake and then we should see a ribbon marking the spot where the trail resumes."

The small group walked carefully through the open swampy area between the bush line and the water. In a short time they found the opening to the path that led to the old trees situated on the distant hill.

Sometime later they came upon the remains of a large cedar tree laying on the ground. None of them had seen a tree with a girth as large. The tree when it stood upright would have been one of the wonders of the forest. John took the time to climb up on the flattened surface on top that was supported by two large limbs not yet rotted. So large was the cedar that he had to use all his strength to gain the top. Perhaps twenty feet or more in circumference, the tree could still be used by animals for homes or retreats. As they moved slowly along the dim path they passed several large yellow birches with one in particular that was monstrous and very, very old. Further on they came on several three hundred year old white pines gently swaying in the breeze.

Dick and Paulette tried to reach around one of the trees from each side and touch fingers. The tree was too great in size and they came up short. The small group wandered about the area, gazing in wonderment that the trees had been able to survive for so many years. Taking a few photos, they rested to regain their stamina and prepared for the trip back to Little Achigan.

The day had become much warmer as they moved through the trees and dense foliage. The trail at times was difficult to follow, but the overhead canopy provided shade from the hot sun. Dick had begun to perspire excessively and was moving much slower. The others patiently waited for him, taking note of his slowing footsteps. Not overly concerned they reasoned that although he was older he was a strong man for his age.

As the group came out into the open Minnow Lake area the mid day sun became intense. Sweat began pouring off John, who seldom lost much body fluid. They walked slowly around the outer edge of the lake stopping occasionally for a rest. As they neared the end of a swampy area, Dick suddenly sat down hard, almost falling on his side. Paulette came and stood beside him.

"What's wrong, Dick?"

"I don't know," he replied. "I'm so weak I can't keep going."

"We should have brought more water," John croaked. He couldn't believe Dick had become this weak in the short time they had been hiking.

"We need to get you out of the sun and into the shade," his wife suggested and knelt beside Dick.

After a few minutes' rest, John helped his friend to his feet.

"I am a little light headed, maybe I can make it down to the boat," he said and began trudging slowly forward.

Taking their time, they descended down the steep, rocky path that followed the creek and after a few short rests the group finally arrived at the edge of the lake.

After drinking a small bottle of water Dick began to cool down in the shade of the overhanging trees.

"I'm still a little weak but not like before. I wonder what happened?"

Looking closely at Dick's heavy shirt, John thought he saw an undergarment beneath it.

"Dick, is that long johns under your flannel shirt?" he asked.

"Yes, I knew it would be cool in the morning coming down the lake so I wore a pair of woollen underwear both on the bottom and top to stay warm," he replied.

"Well, my friend, that explains your dilemma. The heavy clothes caused your body to overheat in the hot sun and with the extra exertion and too little water intake you simply ran out of strength. Small wonder you didn't pass out. Hang on and we'll motor down the lake and you can let the breezes refresh you."

Dick was a physician who relished helping others and dedicated his life to that end. He had come alongside his friend John many years before and helped him through a difficult physical ailment and his friend was always deeply thankful to the generosity and goodness of this caring man.

14. LOST IN THE FOG

Life in the town of Wawa can lead to some interesting and exciting events should either a resident or visitor be ready to challenge the local environment. Roger and Merv were two such individuals who often were found cruising across Lake Superior in their eighteen foot Starcraft boat powered with a 120 hp Mercury Cruiser motor. Their passion and hobby was searching for the beautiful semi-precious gemstone known as agate.

Agates come in many different colours and shapes and can be distinguished from other forms of chalcedony by the bands of different colours that enhance their beauty. The stone is a microcrystalline quartz and are very popular throughout the world and are found in many countries including the United States. Several states, to name only a few, Kentucky, Nebraska, Minnesota and several others have used the agate as their state stone.

When the stones are cut and polished they can be used to make pendants, beads, bolos, and an assortment of other ornamental objects such as animal carvings and bookends. The most well-known place in the world to find and craft these remarkable stones is Idar-Oberstein in Germany since the year 1548. Historically they would be placed in water for cooking or drinking to dispel sickness. However they were also used on the breastplates of warriors in the belief they would give added strength in battle. As well they have been used for their purported healing qualities for various health concerns.

On a particular summer day several decades ago Roger and Merv headed out in their boat across the bay west of Wawa in the direction of Michipicoten Island some thirty seven miles away. One of their favourite agate hunting grounds was an underwater bed only a short distance from the shoreline of the island. The men would locate and collect the agates in their natural state and Merv would take them home and using a cutting tool with a hardened diamond blade, cut the stones into different shapes and sizes.

The day began with a small chop on the water and a mist in the air. Their usual practice was to locate an area deemed a possible agate bed and Merv would remain on board to control the boat as Roger put on his wet suit and snorkel equipment and descend into the dark waters below. Often he would spend eight to ten hours digging the rocks out and bringing them to the surface. Although the diving depth hardly exceeded eight or nine feet, by the end of the day he would be exhausted.

With the throttle open they sped across the open water. The morning sky had a pale yellow glow for the first ten minutes of travel that promised a day of sunshine. Then gradually they began to enter a dense fog bank. Visibility dropped to only a few yards.

At first they weren't concerned as they had been in these conditions many times. They hoped the rising sun would break through and with the help of a little wind the moist grey covering would dissipate quickly. However the fog became increasingly thicker as the miles sped by. The men strained their eyes but were virtually travelling blind hoping not to hit another boat. With only a compass and no guidance system on board they moved forward nervously at a snail's pace.

"Maybe we should have turned back?" Roger said turning to look at his partner. He was a robust man in his twenties who had grown up in the small town and worked at the local iron ore plant. Strong and capable of handling difficult situations, the fog did not discourage him at first, but the longer they were engulfed in the fog, the greater the possibility of a calamity. Neither one could be sure if there were other boats out there.

Merv was a large man with a big voice but he answered with only a mumble that Roger couldn't understand. He was more than twenty years senior to his friend but the two had become friends the last couple of years. He worked as a parts man and millwright at the Algoma Ore mill and many were awed or frightened by his demeanour when they met him or asked for parts. Although the miners were a tough lot on their own, Merv was a man who portrayed strength and a no nonsense attitude. He had served as a midshipman on a frigate in the Atlantic during the Second World War and had been a typical sailor when it came to rough housing in the bars and could more than hold his own. Whether on land or sea, this man seldom showed fear.

Onward they went in the hopes the dense fog would disintegrate but in time they began to realize they were in a situation where they weren't sure where Michipicoten Island was. Although they had a compass and knew they were headed in the general direction of the island they could feel the wind pushing them sideways. They could easily miss the far end and end up out in Lake Superior heading for Thunder Bay.

"I don't like this, Merv. We're too far out now to turn back," Roger said, peering intensely into the fog.

"Yeah, keep going, we'll be there soon," the deep voice came from behind him.

"I wonder how far off course we are?" Roger replied, slowing the boat down. Concern showed on his bewhiskered face. "If we miss the end of the island we could run out of gas and be stranded out in the big lake."

Merv sat still and said nothing. For once he had no harsh response and was deep in thought, his face a mask of granite.

A few more miles crept by when suddenly Roger had a strange feeling come over him. Something was telling him to slow the boat down when a loud shout behind him sent a shiver up his back.

"Stop!" roared his friend, with great urgency in his voice. "Shut 'er down!"

Roger calmly backed off the throttle and turned the engine off. The lapping of the waves against the side of the boat was the only sound they heard. The thick fog lay about them, thicker than Habitant pea soup.

As the boat bounced in the waves the two companions sat quietly staring at each other. Roger wondered why Merv wanted to stop right here.

"What do you think we should do, Merv?"

"Listen, do you hear that?"

From a short distance away a dull noise came through the fog.

"That's the fog horn at the lighthouse. We're at the far end of the island," Roger said with relief. "If we move towards the sound we should be able to see the beacon fairly soon. Good thing we stopped the boat or we would have ended up miles away in the big lake and running out of gas."

The men carefully maneuvered the boat within a mile of shore where they could see the strong light from the tower and anchored down to wait for the day to clear.

Although years have passed since that day, Roger still remembers how amazed he was that at the very moment he felt he should slow down the boat, his friend had yelled for him to stop. Neither one could have heard the fog horn over the roar of the engine or seen the light and so we are left with the mystery. Roger always attributes this moment in time to the hand of God stopping them and will be always thankful.

15. MOOSE ON THE ABINETTE RIVER

In the wilderness area north of the town of Thessalon and south of the town of Chapleau are a multitude of lakes and rivers. Highway 129 is the paved highway that runs between the two towns and has carried hunters and fisherman for more than a century, all with great aspirations and dreams of bagging wild game and fighting fish of all sizes.

There are hundreds of moose stories floating around; memories in the minds of the men who have hunted moose through the years. Many of those stories would involve the tracking, the calling and the shooting of the great monarch, as well as the packing out of the moose through the dense bush of the north. Some of these wonderful stories we seldom have the opportunity to hear. Allow me to relate one story that happened nearly sixty years ago involving two canoes and three young men who travelled into a remote area east of Highway 129 where the Abinette River runs north and west. This story does involve shooting a moose and the wild events that took place during their hunt.

A young man of nineteen by the name of Jack had been raised on a farm in Leeburn, Ontario and had already spent considerable time hunting for various animals including deer, moose and small game. For the past two years he and two other young men had gone north to hunt the majestic moose. Now he waited with great anticipation for the day of departure, cleaning his gun and preparing his equipment.

The old blue half-ton wound its way around the narrow curves of Highway 129 destined for Pichu Lake where the Upper Mississauga Dam and the local Ranger Station were situated. A beat up trailer with two canoes bounced along behind. One was an eighteen foot fiberglass, wide beam canoe good for use as a freighter, which they hoped would transport their moose meat back to the truck. The other canoe was an aluminum sixteen footer, which carried a portion of their supplies.

The early October morning was crisp and sunny with only a slight breeze as the small group pulled into their departure area on the Mississauga River. With the vitality of youth, the three men eagerly loaded their canoes with all the gear and food to keep them going for at least a week. Vic was the oldest and the brother-in-law of Jack, which usually is an asset when things are in the family.

In this case Vic's claim to fame was his shooting ability. He was recognized as the best shot of the three and would gladly take on the responsibility of killing an animal if given the opportunity.

Jack, on the other hand, was perhaps the strongest, made from good Scottish stock and the only one who could swim. Mike, their friend, was a valuable resource after the animal was down as he was able to butcher it and was a hard worker. And so we find the intrepid trio heading across country, through parts of the Mississauga

River, carrying the monstrous canoes. They made their way across a couple of long portages and then up the arm on what was referred to as Long Lake.

Although the trip was difficult, the three men were well up to the task. Jack had been raised on the farm and was strong as a bull. His two friends were nearly as capable when it came to physically challenging the northern bush. Although dog tired, they pushed on past a few more lakes and finally arrived on the northern arm of the Abinette River on the second day.

Camping on the Abinette that night gave the young crew an opportunity to replenish their body strength after the two draining days of paddling and portaging. Throwing up a small three man canvas tent on a flat area close to the river they devoured some of their precious food and before long crawled into their sleeping bags and were soon lost in dreamland. Visions of moose danced in their heads, with the thrill of the hunt vibrating through their body. No thought of the hard work of hauling, gutting and quartering ever entered their minds; they were young, strong and on a mission.

The following morning found the friends motoring up the north branch of the Abinette. Jack ran the small two horsepower Johnson motor on the big square back canoe and depended on Vic in the front seat to watch for hidden snags or submerged rocks in the shallow river.

More than an hour later Mike, seated in the centre of the canoe, quietly pointed to a dark outline on the shore a hundred yards further on.

"Hey fellas," he whispered, "Slow down, that looks like a moose to me."

Jack throttled down the engine and shut it off.

"Vic, I'll paddle us closer and you let me know when you want to shoot," croaked Jack as low as he could.

"Ok Jack, I can hit it from here. Stop paddling and everybody hold still," came Vic's reply.

"Boom! Boom!" Two rifle shots rang out in the morning air. The sound of the Remington 30:06 was deafening to the canoeists as they sat mesmerized, staring ahead with excitement.

The large cow staggered and turned and then collapsed on the shore.

"Great shot, Vic, she died on the spot, and we don't have to track her or carry her out of the bush," sang out Mike excitedly.

The hunters paddled up within a few feet of the fallen animal and sat watching her for movement. She gave a couple of involuntary twitches and expired. The men scanned the bush behind keeping an eye out for another moose, perhaps a bull that could be standing close. Climbing out of the canoe they walked along the brush line in the hopes of seeing a calf or a bull.

"Let's gut the old girl and bleed her out," Vic said as he pulled out a length of rope and a small come-a-long from his packsack.

Several hours later the moose was quartered and wrapped in cheesecloth and hung high in the air from a large limb of a soft maple tree. The nights were dropping down to the freezing mark, but the days were often close to fifty degrees Fahrenheit, which meant they would need to get the meat to the butcher within the next few days.

"Let's leave the meat here and travel up the river another few miles; hopefully we'll see another moose," Jack suggested. Being good farm boys the thrill of the hunt really boiled down to "bringing home the beef," as some would say. The real motivation was to bring home the meat and stock the freezer. Enjoying nature and being in the outdoors for the sheer enjoyment was not part of their make-up; they were there for food.

They all agreed to move up river and piled into the canoe and began to slowly move north on the river. The day was rapidly coming to a close as they made their way north, watching the shoreline ahead, hoping another animal would venture out to have a drink.

As the sun sank in the western sky and the chill of the October evening began to descend, the three hunters agreed to pull in for the night and set up camp. They were dead tired after a long day of work and looked forward to a good night's rest.

"There's a great spot, Jack," Vic pointed to a clearing a hundred yards ahead.

Jack turned the big canoe into shore and edged up on the small beach. "Yes, this will work fine, let's get busy and unload and set up."

Darkness had fallen by the time the men had made camp, cooked supper and now rested on three old stumps that had been cut years long ago.

"I haven't seen a sign of moose or man since we left the quarters down the river," quipped Mike. "Do you think we'll see another moose on the river tomorrow?"

"One never knows, but I can put out a call tonight before we go to bed and maybe we'll get lucky," Vic responded.

"Well guys, I don't know about you, but I'm heading for the sack. All that food we ate has made me tired," Mike mumbled quietly as he stood and moved towards the tent.

The other two men sat for a long time talking about other trips they had made and some old stories they had heard many times before. The hours slipped away as they kept the fire burning, but finally around the midnight hour Vic decided to turn in for the night.

"I'll put out a call, Jack. Are you coming in the tent?"

"No, I'll come to bed shortly, I'm going to stay up for awhile."

Vic put out a loud, long call designed to call in a bull moose. Then he headed for the warmth of his sleeping bag. Jack sat staring at the fire. He didn't feel like going to bed. He felt warm enough in his old Mackinaw jacket and wool cap and felt at peace out here in the wilds. Taking a long stick they had been using, he stoked the embers and was turning to place another small chunk of wood on the fire when he heard a noise a short distance away. The sound came from across a small pond that lay close by. Only a few feet of water in depth, the pool was only a few yards in width.

Jack sat very still. He heard a rustle of leaves as if something was moving along the opposite shore. What was it, he wondered. He reached for his 30:06 Remington and laid it across his lap. Maybe it was wolves. He wished he could see into the deep darkness. Somehow the night seemed colder and his heart began to beat more rapidly. Then came a hollow knocking noise, almost as if someone was taking a stick and hitting a tree sharply. Jack soon real-ized a bull moose was rapping the trees, letting others know he was king of the forest. He recalled old timers telling him about how the bulls would scrape and bang the trees during rutting season.

A moment later he heard a short grunt that electrified him to the core. The blood surged through his body as he realized a rutting moose was only a few yards away. His heart began to accelerate and he could feel his already ruddy complexion turn an even darker red. Not sure what he should do, he threw another small branch in the fire, hoping to make it burn brighter. Maybe he should wake up the guys, but he could hear them snoring softly and decided they needed their sleep.

Time seemed to end for Jack as he sat alone by the fire listening to the hush of the forest. He could hear the faint scratching of a mouse or some other small animal close by. The night was still, and now he waited for the moose to make a noise. It must have stopped to smell and listen. Then he heard a twig snap underfoot. The animal was much closer than before. He waited, frozen to his seat, nervous and fearful at the same time.

Jack's eyes were glued to the dark bush. He wondered if the moose would come close enough for him to see. His face had drawn tight and his hairy eyebrows were knit together in concentration. Time passed slowly and he felt tired, so very tired, but he forced himself to remain alert waiting for the bull to come closer. Indeed he almost sensed the presence of the animal. He found it hard to understand why it had not smelled the human scent or been frightened away by the smell of wood smoke.

A heavy footstep only a few yards behind the tent brought him from his trance. He looked at his watch in the dull light of the fire. Another hour and a half and morning would bring enough light to see. Once more he fed some small white birch pieces into the fire and watched it grow. He reasoned the moose was standing in the darkness watching him, and that was scary. Jack's eyelids began to close as he swayed on the old stump. He needed sleep badly but was determined to wait for the morning light and shoot the moose. He felt chilled and was shaking a little, both from nervousness and the night air.

Once more he heard a loud grunt and then the sound of the moose racks scraping the trees. For the next hour the bull continued making the loud cracking sounds of an enraged animal, and Jack kept his eyes partly open, fearful of passing into dreamland. He had slipped off his seat and lay half on the ground in a fetal position, sometimes with his eyes closing, but every few minutes the sound behind the tent brought him to alertness.

He marvelled at how his two friends were able to sleep through the noise. Finally he decided he must wake them. He crawled to the front door of the little tent and untied the opening.

"Vic, Vic," he croaked, grabbing the end of his brother-in-law's sleeping bag and giving it a shake.

"What?" a sleepy reply came to his ears.

"Get up, there's a moose out here and it's going to be light shortly."

That was all Vic needed to hear. He was instantly awake and pulling on his clothes. Without a word he was out of the tent and listening. Jack had returned to his seat and simply pointed to the area behind their tent. Shaken from the ordeal of the long night and lack of sleep, he knew Vic was far better suited to shoot the animal.

His friend came over and sat on another stump and waited, and sure enough the moose began to bash and tear up the brush once more. The early gray of morning had begun to show through the tops of the trees as the two men sat silently waiting for dawn. Perhaps a half an hour passed and then they saw movement in the darkness and more loud noises. Vic gripped his rifle waiting, extremely tense with anticipation, hoping to see a shadow or outline. And then he saw what he was sure were two eyes staring at him from thirty feet away, so close the two hunters were transfixed.

Although the light of day was still to come, Vic decided to take a shot. He was sure he could see the dark outline of the big bull. The gunshots would certainly awaken Mike in the tent who was still resting peacefully through the racket, but the noise would bring him out of the tent in a hurry.

"Boom! Boom!" The loud report of Vic's 30-06 carbine echoed through the night. Then in that early morning darkness, just as the light of dawn began to spread, Jack and Vic were able to see the dark shadow collapse on the ground. The bull spent the last few minutes of his life thrashing and kicking on the ground, never knowing what had happened. Surely a tragic end to a majestic animal, but to the young men it meant meat for the winter, and they had no remorse.

Mike came rolling out of the tent, his eyes the size of saucers as he looked wildly around. Whereas Jack was completely done in, Mike was full of energy and couldn't believe the sight before him. He stood looking down at the moose in shock, not believing what lay before him.

After a few minutes of explanation, Jack filled his coffee pot with water and restoked the dying fire. His eyes were filmed over and all he could think of was taking a nap, but the other men planned to gut and quarter this second moose right now. Lots of work, and they expected Jack to help.

Our tale could end here with the fellows working most of the day preparing for the trip back down the river except for an unfortunate event that was to drain our young man Jack to the point of exhaustion and pneumonia. Even the strongest and healthiest can be pushed beyond the limit of endurance. Thus we find our intrepid trio loading the big eighteen foot canoe with several packages of the moose, which they had skinned and de-boned.

The middle of the afternoon found them heading down the Abinette River to where they had left the four quarters of the first moose. Quite pleased with themselves, they paddled silently along in the big canoe, trailing the aluminum canoe behind that held most of their gear.

In a short time they came on the site of the first kill and made their way to the hanging quarters. All seemed to be well and they carried each piece of meat depositing them with the other meat in the large canoe. They realized the load was heavy but felt they could easily transport everything safely back to the truck in one trip. With only a few short hours left of daylight it was imperative to make it to Long Lake, part of the Mississauga River where they planned to spend the night. They all knew this would entail two long hard portages through the rough terrain before night.

As Jack steered the big canoe into a set of small rapids near the end of the north branch of the Abinette, he felt as if the stern had moved too far to the centre of the rapids. The force of the water pushed the canoe further than he wished, and as he gave more gas to the outboard they soon were hurtling downstream on an angle. Unfortunately the meat had shifted and Mike tried to shift his weight in the centre. As they moved into the shallowest part of the rapids, he suddenly felt the craft stall and begin to tip. Jack shifted his weight in the back but Mike sitting on the moose meat was sent flying into the water. A moment later, Jack and Vic joined him as the canoe flipped over, sending all their moose meat, their rifles, gas can and extras to the bottom of the river.

A catastrophe of gigantic proportions for the young fellows, after all the work and effort put into the hunt. The three managed to swim to shore, struggling to cope with the disaster. Jack, true to form, with no sleep and already exhausted from two long days of butchering moose and staying awake for two days and a night, now agreed to swim after the canoes that had travelled on downstream in the current.

The young man was chilled from the immersion and with the water so cold he left on his clothes and floated downstream. Perhaps the greatest blessing was he could see the canoes caught in the shrubs only two hundred yards away. That proved to be a major help as they could have been swept far downstream which would have taken a long time to retrieve. In a few moments he swam close to the canoes and grabbed the largest by the gunwales. Making his way to the stern he pulled a rope through the front hole and began to walk back upstream towing the pair of canoes behind him. Although Jack was young, the two hundred yard pull upstream through the current took much of his strength.

Mike trudged downstream to meet him and helped pull the canoes back to where Vic stood. Meanwhile, Vic was keeping an eye on the spot where the meat and rifles had fallen in. He stood with a grim expression on his face trying to figure out the best way to retrieve everything.

"That's where the moose is, fellows, and the rifles," said Vic, pointing to a spot in the river.

Disappointment could be seen on their faces. They stood in the water up to their knees with a look of despondency, lost in their thoughts. Soaking wet and bedraggled looking, no one uttered a sound.

Finally Jack spoke up. "I'll go down and try to find the rifles, the river's not too deep right here."

"I'm going to drain the motor first, men, and try to get it going while you look for those guns and moose," rasped Vic as he moved towards the outboard motor.

Jack had revived after the dunking and retrieved a long piece of rope from the one canoe and prepared to swim to the dump site. His face was gaunt and pale as he waded further out in the cold water and then disappeared beneath. After several attempts he came up with one rifle.

Mike came out to meet him, taking the rifle and handing Jack a log pick that had been left on shore from the days when the logs were run down river. "Here Jack, try hooking this into the quarters of the moose and then tie it off and bring back the loose end of the rope. I will haul it into shore and put it in the canoe."

For the next hour, Jack dove several times, retrieving the rifles and the meat by hooking the big pick into the meat and letting the other men haul in their precious cargo. With each passing moment and each dive, Jack came closer and closer to collapse and yet he managed to bring back from the watery depths every article lost in the spill. With the final piece salvaged, Jack staggered ashore and sat down, so weak he wondered if he had the strength to keep going. Changing his wet clothes, he shook a little from the exposure but determined not to give in.

"I have the motor running, maybe we can travel a few miles before dark?" Vic rasped, more of a guttural grunt. He also was nearing his physical limit of endurance. He looked over at Jack and what he saw gave him concern. His brother-in-law looked like death warmed over. "Yeah, I think I remember a good spot downriver. Do you think you can make it, Jack?"

"Sure, let's go, but stay still, we don't want to capsize again."

Once more situated in the large canoe with all the meat loaded, they pushed off and headed for the nearest good campsite they could find.

The fellows did make it home safely in two days with all the meat, and Jack recovered fully after two weeks with a bout of pneumonia. Perhaps only a strong young farm boy could recover from such an ordeal.

16. FEARFUL MOMENTS

The storm was wreaking havoc in the wilderness north of Sault Ste. Marie. Trees were cracking and snapping off in the wild wind of August. Others were being ripped up by their roots and flung on the ground. This was not a night to be heading on the back roads to camp. The highway to the small village of Searchmont was closed due to a washout. All this seemed to mean nothing to two trucks with three couples intent on driving to a camp on Achigan Lake. In the first vehicle, a Nissan Pathfinder, Les and John in the front seat led the way with their wives, Louise and Mary in the backseat. Lorne and his wife Judy followed close behind in their half ton truck.

John had a vague feeling that potential disaster awaited them as they took a circuitous route by way of Highway 129 and down the Ranger Lake road that would enable them to reach the old logging road that led to the cabin. They had left late in the evening and night time was rapidly approaching. He only hoped there would be no big trees down blocking the way.

Hours later found the small gang of campers slowly driving down the back dirt road. Uncountable pot holes filled with water dotted the road. The trees lining the road swayed in the wind. Although the wind had decreased greatly they were watching for limbs that could break off and land on them. The fall storms had begun, bringing the wind and rain with warm temperatures and they knew they needed to be prepared for unexpected events along the way.

At the top of a rise, John's heart leapt in his throat. Suddenly the road disappeared and only a black abyss appeared ahead. Frantically he stomped on the brakes and the truck slid sideways in the mud filled road. With a thumping heart he stared ahead into a shiny void.

Les, his friend was sitting next to him in the front seat and had only moments before asked John to drive for a spell. Now he too was fearful of what appeared to be a deep black pit ahead. As John calmed down, a feeling of foolishness swept over him. His eyes began to focus in the dark and he realized what he was looking at was an optical illusion. The road had not disappeared as he had feared but rather it was covered in black water and when the lights of the truck skimmed over the top, it appeared as a great black hole. They now were in total darkness and the lightning and thunder had subsided as they crept slowly forward avoiding the debris on the road from falling branches. Occasionally they had to stop to pull a large limb out of the way and with the visibility so limited they had to be careful not to slide into a water filled ditch on either side.

As they came to within a mile of the camp, John once again jammed on the brakes. This time, although not as scary, the problem was very real. A huge maple tree lay across their path. Everyone exited the vehicles to take a look. This was a monstrous tree and would need a lot of cutting to clear a way through. Without hesitation Lorne walked to the back of his truck and brought out his big chainsaw and went to work. He was an old logger at heart and relished the opportunity to be of service. As he cut one branch after another, the others began hauling away the cut limbs. Working above his head he cleared a path under the main trunk to drive under. The tree had stretched across the road and the trunk was suspended by gigantic limbs holding it high in the air. Finally he finished and the road was passable once more.

The two trucks skimmed under the high arch and they joyfully tooled on to their destination arriving at 2 a.m. The trip which had begun with an element of excitement was finally over but the morrow would bring a special type of challenge for one person in particular.

The following morning after a late breakfast, Les and Louise set up a small two man tent on the front lawn. They wished to completely feel they were getting the full wilderness experience. Putting their light sleeping bags and pillows inside the tent they made a decision to take a boat and go fishing. The day was sunny and warm and they slowly trolled around the lake enjoying the gentle breeze on the water. The day seemed perfect, especially after they caught a good sized lake trout that would make a good meal at supper. As they passed a reclusive beach in a far bay they went ashore to lay on the sand and soak in the rays, little realizing that devilish minds were at work back at camp.

In the world of outdoors there are many little animals and insects that can be intriguing but also cause discomfort and annoyance. For some such as Louise, pests such as ants, spiders and snakes can cause untold grief and panic in a not so perfect world. Such would soon be the case as one devious minded soul unzipped the couple's front screen on their tent and entered. He, and it was a he, had a long rubber worm normally used as bait for bass fishing and placed it inside the smaller sleeping bag that had ladies' articles around it.

For those of a gentler nature, this kind of prank is nearly unforgivable; however for the others inside the cabin they could hardly wait for the fireworks to begin once their friend slid into her sleeping bag. Louise was known for her excitable high strung nature, and so the four inside the camp were waiting to hear the screams and antics when her bare skin touched the cold rubber worm.

The day wore on and the party of six had a night time fire after supper and reminisced of fun times long past. However as the evening wore on they all decided to go to bed for a good night's rest.

John and Mary with Lorne and Judy scurried inside the cabin and kept their eyes focused on the tent outside as their friends disappeared from view inside the tent. There were lots of giggles and laughter from both the tent and the cabin, but for totally different reasons. Disappointment can come in many forms and on this night the four sets of eyes grew weary of waiting as the lights went out inside the thin walled shelter and no yelling or screaming had been forthcoming.

The following morning arrived bright and warm. The aroma of good coffee had brought Lorne out first to sit in a rocking chair on the screened front porch and watch the lake. Within minutes the others joined him with their steaming hot coffee to relax and discuss what they would do for the day. Les had come out of the tent and made his way to the cabin and came to sit on the porch with the other four.

Louise, his loving wife had headed directly for the outhouse situated fifty yards behind the main cabin. She had made a special sign for the front door that read "Relax in the Loo." As a woman who enjoyed making things more appealing she was always actively engaged in upgrading her surroundings in whatever way she could. As she headed through the wooden door she felt pleased with her handiwork and felt at home; even pleasantly at peace with the world, so to speak.

As the five individuals on the front porch drank their coffee and marvelled at the beauty of the surrounding hills and the stillness of the lake, there was a special tranquility and peacefulness that comes only from being close to nature. Suddenly the small group were jolted from their quiet moment when a piercing scream came from the old outhouse, aka "the Loo."

Everyone on the deck sat bolt upright with pounding hearts. All the small animals within hearing range scurried for their hidden burrows. Even the ducks, a family of mergansers swimming by, skittered off with their wings flapping vigorously.

"What's that?" Lorne asked, putting down his cup, and readied himself for action. The screaming and frantic yelps were coming closer as Les prepared to go see if his wife had hurt herself or seen a wild animal. As he opened the porch door and started down the stairs, Louise came running around the corner of the cabin and headed directly for him. Each one stared at the distraught, aggravated lady as she ran into her husband's arms, wondering what could have caused her to freak out in such a manner.

All kinds of thoughts went through the minds of the observers as they gazed in wonderment. No one could fathom her distress, as Les sat back down in his chair with his wife on his lap trying to calm her. Whimpering and crying she tried to tell her hair raising story through intermittent sobs. To those around her some questions had come to mind and some smiles had begun to show on their faces. Each one knew their friend could be high strung at times and she did look somewhat comical but they tried to mask their thoughts on what appeared to them as a hilarious situation. Unfortunately the men especially couldn't keep a twinkle out of their eyes, and Louise was quick to pick up on this. Although Les had no idea what had transpired, some of the others began to guess what may have happened.

A small tinkle of mirth began to grow into uproarious laughter the further the poor distraught woman went into her narrative. She began to tell of her encounter with what she thought was a small, oily snake like creature as she plunked down on the seat and prepared to read one of the magazines nearby. She suddenly had felt a weird, crawling sensation on her bare leg and she jumped up and total fear came over her as she saw a brown coloured snake of some sort flying through the air. The poor visibility inside the outhouse may have helped her react so violently in seeing this unknown, perhaps life threatening species of reptile.

John and the others sadly could not restrain themselves as finally the episode they hoped would develop had finally occurred. Louise was quick to realize something was amiss and started to interrogate each one. At first she was angry with her husband for not being more compassionate of her situation but soon understood he had simply got caught up in the moment of laughter with the others. However, she was quick to perceive everyone knew something she didn't. Although no one ever has ever admitted to this outlandish prank or as some would call it mischievous joke, the lady in question certainly feels she knows who did this terrible thing.

After some time, life came back to normal for all involved and it was not necessary to take Louise to the hospital to have her heart checked after this heart stopping moment. Les had gone out to the danger area to check if the wild thing was still around but he found no trace of the foresaid life threatening worm-like serpent.

Forgiveness for some things come slowly but eventually all would be well in the relationships of friends, but never forgotten would be the moment of great fear, the screaming and the laughter that followed for this dear lady.

And for all of those who enjoy the experiences of the wilderness we can all sympathize with what transpired that day as each one has encountered moments of terror and fear when seeing bloodsuckers on their feet or bumblebees on their legs or huge green snakes slither between their feet.

How many can remember those heart stopping moments? And so ends our little tale of adventure on the road and in the loo. Hoping your next trip to the outhouse is not as traumatic as it was for the lady known as Lou.

The Author

17. THE OLD MAN AND THE STUMP

The stump sat on a hill, a small rise that overlooked a seldom visited lake. The stump had a quality all of its own. An air of loneliness enveloped the weather beaten upright as it sat by itself with very little vegetation close by. How many years had the stump been there? How many years since the wood cutter cut down the large tree that belonged to the stump? One could only guess at the age as it was covered in a dark green-black covering of moss.

There was a man who often visited the lake, sometimes to canoe, sometimes to fish and always to sit on the stump, to relax and enjoy the peaceful setting. The man had grown to love the stump. Perhaps the word *love* was too strong. He had learned to enjoy seeing the stump as he coasted by in his canoe. He found a certain kind of joy in wondering how many people over the years had taken time to climb the slight incline and sit on the stump. On every trip to the lake he would make his way up from the shore, usually at lunch time, and take a good look at it. Then, if there had been no rain, he would sit down and gaze out on the water. Should the stump be damp he would often fold his jacket or place a small cushion over it to keep his backside dry. It was just the right size in height and circumference for him and for some unknown reason did not have jagged wooden edges that could stick him.

Today found the man alone, once again visiting the lake. He had brought a small cooler with snacks and drinks in an old prospector's packsack.

Although the carry-in was only a few hundred yards it was becoming harder as the years went by. His rod and reel and paddles and net were tied up tightly on the inside of the canoe. Sometimes he brought his fly rod but usually his spinning outfit. He enjoyed paddling the lake and usually he trolled a small lure behind.

The day was perfect for the man. The sun was warm and he felt a slight breeze off the water as he came near the water's edge. He was thinking how nice it would be to catch a small trout, perhaps only a foot long, and fry it up near the stump.

He had brought a small frying pan and a spatula and some butter and salt and pepper. Looking down the lake he could see two loons swimming in his direction. They had become accustomed to his visits and often would swim in front of him as he sat passively on the stump. Twice he had brought a small camera and photographed them. They often called out in their thrilling staccato cry that sent chills down his back. Perhaps they were lonely as they seldom saw human visitors.

The man always questioned why so few came to fish or canoe this lake. The fishing could be good at times. He had caught fish here over the years, not a lot and usually not over twelve or fourteen inches in length. However, every now and again a two or three pounder would strike and give him a glorious battle. He never kept the big ones any longer. He would carefully release them while they were alongside the canoe in the hopes they would survive. Only brook trout inhabited this small lake.

He always took time to gaze at them and marvel at the beauty of their speckles as they glistened in the sunlight.

And so on this particular day he arrived on the shore and prepared his fishing gear for his time on the water. Peering down the lake all was peaceful. He took a look to his left along the western shore and could make out the stump, still sitting there as it always did. He wondered if the stump would outlast him. He hoped so. The lake would not be the same without this solitary soldier overlooking the water and being in the perfect spot to sit on and have lunch. Many the time he had sat on the ground and rested his back against the stump and fallen into a restful slumber.

The man pushed his canoe off shore. A slight breeze had sprung up from out of the west sending the bow of the canoe sideways. He felt warm after the portage and took his hat off and ran his fingers through his thinning white hair. The wind felt good on the scalp and his energy began to return. Picking up a paddle he effortlessly stroked through the small waves as he headed for a bay halfway down the lake.

Two hours elapsed in what seemed a very short time. He had caught three trout and released the largest one. Two he kept and would fry them up once he made it back to the end of the lake where the stump sat. He would have a small meal of the fish and a small quantity of rice and a cup of green tea, then consider taking a nap. The man angled his canoe towards the western bank and began his turn to head back. He thought he saw movement at the other end and what appeared like a flash of light. Visitors? His mind dwelled on these things as he paddled slowly along. Casting a fuzzy looking lure far out behind the canoe he decided to troll back through the deepest part of the lake. One could never tell if there might be a big old cruiser near the bottom of the lake, but his mind was now on lunch and spending time on his favourite spot.

Halfway back his fishing rod suddenly jerked savagely and almost flew out of the canoe as his reel began to scream. Excitedly he grabbed the rod and waited for a second and then set the hook solidly. He could feel the weight of the fish as it fought for freedom. This was no average size fish. This felt like the largest fish he had ever caught. The battle continued for some time, with the fish at first stripping off line but soon allowing him to regain some. The trout fought desperately in a valiant attempt to shake free from the foreign object that kept it moving upwards. And then the fight was over. A landing net dipped deep into the water and with one great lift the struggling trout was out of the water and into the centre of the canoe.

The white haired man could only sit and stare at the beautiful multi-coloured fish that lay before him. Without question the fish was the biggest brook trout he had ever caught. He was stunned. What was he to do? Perhaps he should take a photo of it and then release this magnificent specimen and let it live out its final years in the wild lake. Then again he could take it home and eat it. Or take it and have it mounted? Wouldn't that fish look grand on his rec room wall? He smiled as he gently lifted the massive fish from the net with a gloved hand and placed it in the water beside the canoe. He stroked it softly helping it regain its strength. What a fighter, he thought, as the big fish slowly swam away.

Suddenly he felt famished. No more fishing, he felt better than he had for a long time. Growing old had its drawbacks: less energy, less strength and less willpower but today had rekindled the old flame of life and the desire to enjoy all that God had provided for mankind's use.

Looking south down the lake he could see definite movement now. There was no doubt there was some kind of activity on the small hill where the stump was. Something shining in the sunlight meant it was humans, but why had they gone there first and not out fishing? He had seen movement and the flash of light some time ago so they had been there a while.

Putting away his equipment, he slowly moved towards the end of the lake. Drawing closer he confirmed there were indeed people on the hill moving around. He stopped paddling and sat still, wondering what he should do. His plan of resting on the stump and frying the fish could not happen with them there. For the first time in all the years of coming here he would be stymied in spending time on the stump. In the past he had seen one or two canoes on the water, and had seen evidence of someone being on the hill but today he was unable to have his lunch and a quiet time of relaxation. Something close to anger rose in his heart. A bag of mixed feelings went through him. The reasonable thing to do was go say hello as it was not far from the portage trail but some inner turmoil held him back. He did not want to go near them.

As the man looked on he could make out several people. They seemed to be different sizes, probably a family, but why did they not go out fishing or canoeing like any normal humans would? His canoe had drifted into a small bay but he had not noticed. Taking out a small pair of binoculars he focused on the hill with the stump. The binoculars were old and not the strongest by any means, but after considerable adjusting he brought the group into focus. Two children and two adults were standing around looking at the ground. Then he realized what was going on. They had started a very small fire not far from the stump. He could make out thin tendrils of smoke beginning to rise in the air as the father laid some kind of fire starter in the grass and small twigs they had collected.

As the fisherman watched through the glasses he became mesmerized by the activity. He broke his concentration when a thought struck him. He was invading these peoples private lives, which was wrong. What should he do? Taking one last look, he saw the man pick up an object. Wait a moment, is that an axe? What does he plan to do now? The answer came quickly. The father was chipping away at the sides of the stump. As the pieces came flying off the sides the children began to gather them and place them in the fire. The old man's heart seemed to stop, his breathing came in short gasps as he witnessed the violation of his beloved stump. Stunned he lowered his spy glasses and put them away in his sack.

Sitting there in his small canoe with sadness written on his face, his mind began to recall the many years of enjoyment he'd had on the lake, sitting on the stump, cooking up lunch and the wonderful fishing. Suddenly the realization struck him like a bolt from heaven. He had become old with a degree of sentimentality often attached with aging. Deep thoughts invaded his mind as he sat with his head bowed.

The time had come for him to move on. All good things come to an end.

This was the way ordained for man and nature. The world was in constant change, and all humans must accept those changes. Who was he to think he had sole right to this little piece of paradise?

God the great Creator had made nature to be enjoyed and used by all generations. The time had come for a new young family to enjoy what he had been blessed to use for so many years. He knew in his heart the end was near, not only for the stump but for him as well. The family would undoubtedly destroy the stump in order to make room for a small tent so they could spend a night or two on the lake. This would bring a significant change to the lake but one that would have great meaning for a family who enjoyed the outdoors. With his head still bowed, he gave thanks for the many years he had been allowed to come.

Picking up his paddle, the man in the canoe began to angle towards the entrance of the portage. He had proposed in his mind not to invade the family's private time and only waved to them from a distance as he came closer. They all stood and waved back. A surge of emotion crept over him as he moved closer to the trail leading to his truck. He knew this would be his final trip to this wonderful little lake. A real fisherman would still come in order to enjoy the fishing, but he had come for so much more, as he recalled the peacefulness and the tranquility and the special times he had spent on the stump. Memories would always be there of those special moments of catching fish, eating fish and simply sitting on the stump in deep thought. With one last look back, he said his final farewell to the lake and the stump.

CPSIA information can be obtained
at www.ICGtesting.com
Printed in the USA
BVHW090159180321
602786BV00006B/368

9 781460 006078